VOLUME
13

Originally published in the United Kingdom in weekly parts **COMBAT & SURVIVAL**
is a study of the armed forces at work. It shows the skills taught to soldiers
and the way in which military units operate. It examines the weapons
and equipment used by different armies; and, by looking at recruit
training and exercises, **COMBAT & SURVIVAL** demonstrates
how the armed forces develop individual responsibility,
leadership and initiative.

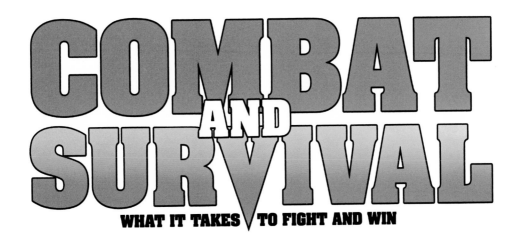

COMBAT AND SURVIVAL

WHAT IT TAKES TO FIGHT AND WIN

VOLUME
13

H. S. STUTTMAN, INC. *publishers*   Westport, Connecticut 06889

Contents
Volume 13

Published by H. S. STUTTMAN INC.
Westport, Connecticut 06889
© Aerospace Publishing 1991
ISBN 0-87475-560-3

1P(1632)30

ATTACKING GUERRILLA CAMPS

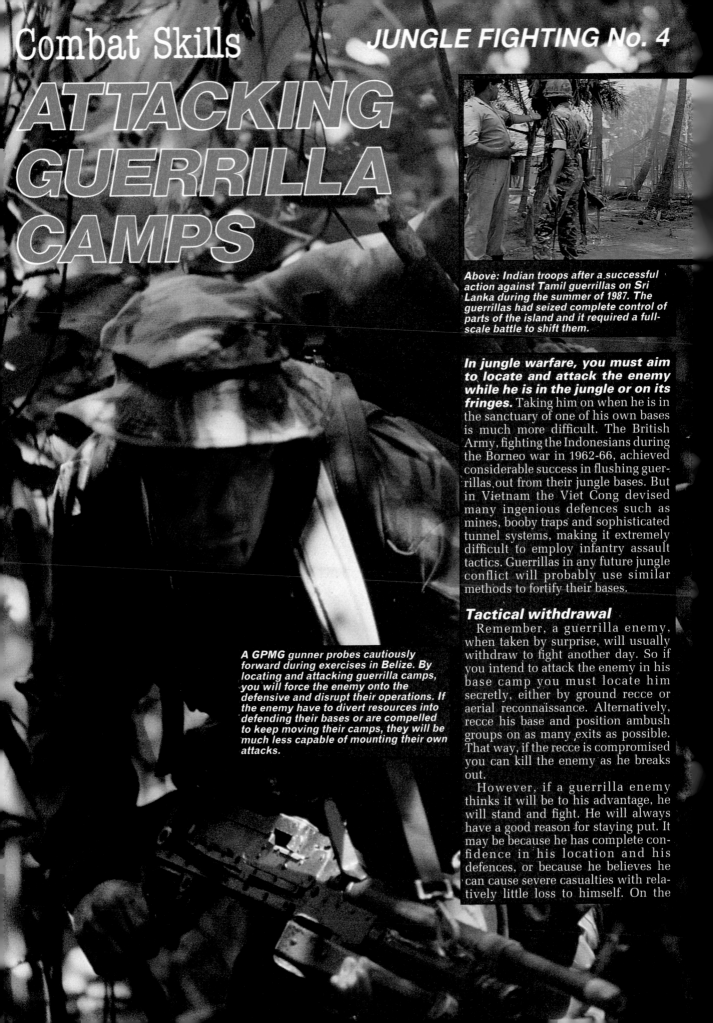

Above: Indian troops after a successful action against Tamil guerrillas on Sri Lanka during the summer of 1987. The guerrillas had seized complete control of parts of the island and it required a full-scale battle to shift them.

In jungle warfare, you must aim to locate and attack the enemy while he is in the jungle or on its fringes. Taking him on when he is in the sanctuary of one of his own bases is much more difficult. The British Army, fighting the Indonesians during the Borneo war in 1962-66, achieved considerable success in flushing guerrillas out from their jungle bases. But in Vietnam the Viet Cong devised many ingenious defences such as mines, booby traps and sophisticated tunnel systems, making it extremely difficult to employ infantry assault tactics. Guerrillas in any future jungle conflict will probably use similar methods to fortify their bases.

Tactical withdrawal

Remember, a guerrilla enemy, when taken by surprise, will usually withdraw to fight another day. So if you intend to attack the enemy in his base camp you must locate him secretly, either by ground recce or aerial reconnaissance. Alternatively, recce his base and position ambush groups on as many exits as possible. That way, if the recce is compromised you can kill the enemy as he breaks out.

However, if a guerrilla enemy thinks it will be to his advantage, he will stand and fight. He will always have a good reason for staying put. It may be because he has complete confidence in his location and his defences, or because he believes he can cause severe casualties with relatively little loss to himself. On the

A GPMG gunner probes cautiously forward during exercises in Belize. By locating and attacking guerrilla camps, you will force the enemy onto the defensive and disrupt their operations. If the enemy have to divert resources into defending their bases or are compelled to keep moving their camps, they will be much less capable of mounting their own attacks.

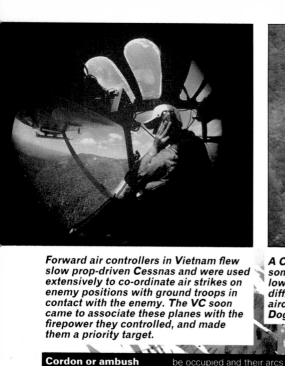

Forward air controllers in Vietnam flew slow prop-driven *Cessnas* and were used extensively to co-ordinate air strikes on enemy positions with ground troops in contact with the enemy. The VC soon came to associate these planes with the firepower they controlled, and made them a priority target.

A *Cessna O-2 flies low over a hamlet some where in South Vietnam. Flying low at treetop height made them a difficult target for ground fire. This aircraft supplemented the Cessna Bird Dog for Forward Air Control use.*

other hand, he may want to gain time for the evacuation of stores, ammunition or guerrilla leaders from the area. Most dangerous of all, he may wish to pin you down while other guerrilla forces mount a flanking action. So always ask yourself *why* the enemy is not following normal guerrilla tactics.

Jungle guerrillas have, since the Vietnam war, developed the technique of building defended villages. These are strongholds constructed in enemy territory among difficult ter-

Fighter ground attack
If the target is beyond artillery range, 81-mm mortars can be manpacked to within range. If the target can be accurately marked, air support can be called in. The Harrier is ideal for this type of close air support operation.

Cordon or ambush groups
Ambush groups must be in position well before the main body move up to the start line, and must understand the position to be occupied and their arcs of fire to prevent blue-on-blue contacts. They must move into position without alerting the enemy, as this is the most vulnerable phase of the attack.

The breaching party
They will need an adequate supply of grenades, satchel charges and perhaps Bangalore torpedoes for breaching wire. They may need assault pioneer help.

Flamethrowers
Flamethrowers are invaluable in this sort of operation as their short range means that they can be used without fear of hitting your supporting units. Flame warfare has a considerable shock effect on the enemy and will help minimise your own casualties.

Fire support
Use all the available support to maximum effect to suppress the enemy while the breaching party breaks in and while the assaulting sections fight through. GPMGs in the sustained fire role, 51-mm mortars, 66-mm light anti-tank weapons, grenade launchers and 81-mm mortars should be used to saturate the area in front of the troops as they assault.

rain. Do not confuse defended villages with nominally friendly or neutral villages in which the enemy has taken refuge. Where innocent locals are involved, an assault is clearly out of the question. Instead you will need to mount a cordon and search operation.

Defended villages usually have a warning system, involving informers, ambushes, observation posts and patrols. There will be minefields, punjis and defended positions on the approaches, and possibly bamboo fences surrounding it. Within will be protected houses, more booby traps, and a tunnel system to enable the inhabitants to survive an artillery bombardment, or air attack, or to escape into the jungle. So do not underestimate the difficulties of assaulting such a position. If an assault by fire is possible, then you should attempt it. If it is out of range for artillery, use mortars.

The great advantage of this technique is that it minimises casualties,

A Chinese communist propaganda poster produced at the height of the Cultural Revolution. Note the two-pronged approach to progress: Chairman Mao's Little Red Book and the AK-47 assault rifle.

ATTACKING A GUERRILLA CAMP

The key to success is maintaining surprise, more so than in most other types of operation: in guerrilla warfare the enemy will not sit around to fight on your terms. He fully expects his campaign to last 20 or 30 years, so you have got to make sure he does not escape to fight another day.

Bombing
If the enemy has had time to prepare, his bunkers will give him protection from shelling and bombing. However, the shelling will prevent him from moving on the surface and should cause casualties before he takes cover. Heavy preparatory bombardment will detonate mines and booby traps and generally degrade the village defences.

Blast the water
Grenade or satchel-charge the village pond or any other stretches of water: this will bring any enemy hiding there to the surface.

ghting through
u must be thorough: treat very house as occupied by emy, and clear it as per e drill. Check every inch, it could hide the entrance a bunker or tunnel system at could mean enemy pearing behind you and ing some real damage. enade every entrance you d, and then leave it uarded.

Assault by fire
From the infantryman's point of view, fire support is the better option as it does not involve fighting through a heavily mined and booby-trapped area covered with enemy bunkers. This method is a stand-off attack where you do the damage with artillery, mortar and small arms fire without entering the village. But if the enemy is well dug in with tunnel systems, you will have to do it the hard way.

Grenade posting
When posting grenades into bunkers, remember that the firing ports in the bunker will channel the grenade blast, so after posting roll away to avoid a faceful!

Gas traps
In Vietnam, many of the VC tunnel systems had a water duck so that gas pumped into them by US tunnel rats would not fill the whole system.

Tunnel systems
You will usually require engineer help to deal with these properly: these are the enemy's escape routes and will be liberally sowed with booby-traps and demolition charges to slow you down if you try to follow him up.

727

HOW TO CLEAR AN ENEMY-FORTIFIED VILLAGE

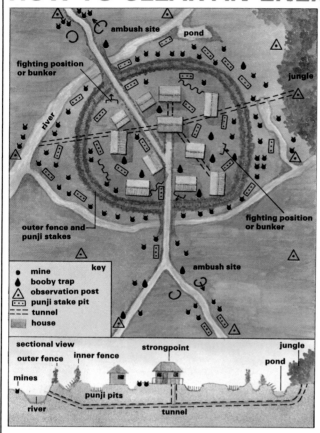

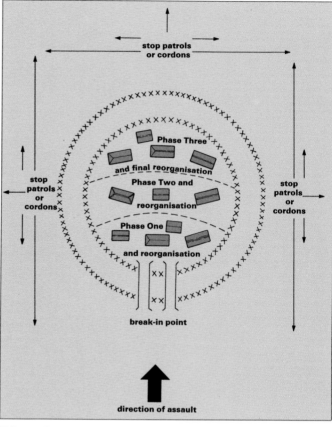

The fortified village

A village fortified to this extent is going to provide any attacking force with some problems. The village is virtually surrounded by water obstacles, and the approach routes to the village are covered by observation posts and prepared and protected ambush positions, which would be hurriedly occupied when warned by the OPs of enemy approach.

Planning the assault

The essential feature of this type of attack is maintaining surprise. The stop patrols and cordons must be in position and ready before the assault group crosses the start line, and after breaking in the position must be cleared in phases with reorganisation at the end of each phase.

but it is ineffective if the village has bunkers, trench systems and tunnels. In Vietnam, the Viet Cong was constantly subjected to intensive aerial bombardment, delivered by fleets of B-52s, only to emerge unscathed to face the subsequent infantry assault. So you will often have no choice but to physically assault enemy defended villages. How do you do this?

First, plan every detail. Gather information on the enemy's defences, his strength, his weapons, his intentions and so on. Make sure you have the maximum fire support available – artillery, mortars, direct-fire 'bunker buster' weapons, and air support. You must break in quickly. If you lose

With their ability to operate away from conventional airfields, the RAF Harriers are ideal for jungle operations. This is one of the four aircraft deployed in the defence of Belize.

Right: The value of light armour in jungle operations was demonstrated in Vietnam. These British Scorpions are on exercise in Belize, where they would provide vital fire support for the infantry.

momentum, the enemy's defences will bog you down. And, most important of all, surprise him. If you don't, the enemy will either have gone, or he will give you a bloody nose. Remember, the 'bush telegraph' is very efficient.

Breach the defences

Having succeeded in getting your men, undiscovered, into an assault position, the next stage is to breach the defences. This can be done by an air strike, using rockets and bombs, or with artillery and mortars. But these methods will be protracted, giving the enemy plenty of warning, so the most effective method is to use anti-tank weapons or flamethrowers or explosive devices, like the Baby Viper or Bangalore Torpedo.

Secure a bridgehead

The assault force must move in closely behind the breaching party, and storm through into the village. If you have achieved total surprise, this should all be possible. Remember, the break-in must be on a narrow front with a limited objective. Aim to secure a bridgehead inside the perimeter from which you can work outwards. You may need engineer or assault pioneer support for this, and, if the terrain allows, armoured support. You will always need supporting fire from machine-guns, M79 grenade-launchers and possibly 66-mm LAWs.

The next stage is to clear the village. Under enemy fire it is difficult to tell which huts are occupied by the enemy and which are not, so you will have to treat all huts as enemy occupied until after the clearance operation. As with any fighting in built-up areas, clear each district before starting on the next one. Otherwise the enemy will reappear behind you, either by lying low in a hut or by using a tunnel system.

Destroy the tunnels

Tunnel clearance is extremely time-consuming, dangerous and complex. But the guerrilla will usually not defend his tunnel system: if he tries to, he will probably incur casualties, and so will have little chance of escaping, especially if a cordon is set up. Occupied or not, tunnel systems should be destroyed by specialists. Engineers have developed various techniques of

forcing gas and non-toxic smoke into tunnels, then the tunnels can be demolished using explosives.

When all opposition has ceased, you will have to search the village and the surrounding countryside. It is essential to have a thorough knowledge of the various hides used by guerrillas in jungles, swamps, ponds, rivers, paddy fields or anywhere else. Never underestimate the enemy's capacity for tunnelling, or for remaining submerged in filthy water by breathing through a bamboo pipe or straw. Your aim will be to capture concealed guerrillas, arms dumps, printing machines, leaflets and any other guerrilla supplies.

Throughout your operation, you will need cordon and ambush groups to isolate an enemy position, prevent it being reinforced and, most important, to intercept any escape attempt. Site these groups with great care,

Many villages in Vietnam had cellars or dug-outs where the locals could hide from bombing or shelling. They could also be used to hide VC or their supplies. Here an officer from 101st Airmobile Division examines a shelter in the Bong Son district.

ensuring that their arcs of fire do not in any way endanger you and your men.

Attacking a guerrilla-defended village is probably one of the most demanding operations that you will ever have to undertake. It needs a lot of soldiers, detailed planning, careful preparation, accurate intelligence, suitable weapons for a break-in and, above all, guts and determination.

You must plan your withdrawal as carefully as the rest of the operation. It is a favourite guerrilla tactic to hit you as, flushed with success and with your guard down, you depart the area. Either leave by helicopter, or, if you have to go on foot, use a different route and keep your wits about you.

Combat Report

Vietnam:
Helicopter Engagement Part 1

For self-preservation, many crew chiefs began arming their helicopters with M60s or Brownings.

Mike Greenwood served as a door gunner with the 117th Aviation Company in Vietnam in the early 1960s. The role of the helicopter force was, officially, to transport the ARVN in and out of firefights with VC guerrillas . . .

Teddy Knapp – a huge black man from Chicago – and a couple of other experienced guys had been the first to rig M60 machine-guns in the right-hand doorways of our UH-1A and UH-1B Huey helicopters. We'd gotten into the practice of using the gun – the "hog", we called it – to suppress Viet Cong fire at a landing zone. This was not exactly cricket in mid-1964 because we were billed as "advisers" and the ARVN (South Vietnamese) were supposed to be doing the fighting.

In July 1964, it was decided that our unit, the 117th Aviation Company, would be broken up and the choppers scattered at smaller LZs, closer to the fighting. When Teddy heard this, he said, "Moe, man, if we get out there in the sticks and divide up our force, we are gonna get our butts chewed. This is not the way to use our choppers."

We slept under the choppers

"I think the major is going to be pretty insistent on it," I goaded.

"We go out. We come back. We drop some ARVN troops in an area where they can ambush Charlie. Charlie ambushes them. It don't make no sense," Knapp complained. "I'm telling you, Moe. I got a feeling. We split up the choppers and make smaller assaults, we're gonna lose the edge. If I go out and fight this way, I am going to come back dead."

Back home, we'd rehearsed using dozens of choppers to move hundreds of men. Now, said the Higher-Ups, we were going to move platoons, or even squads, using only a handful of Hueys at a time.

Knapp and I had been trained not as gunners but as crew chiefs. He was responsible for a Huey named Checkers, while the pilot of my ship had Iron Lady painted on the nose.

On a wet, sticky Tuesday afternoon we pulled out of Qui Nhon and climbed westward toward a laager 40 miles inland where we were to rendezvous with a small force of ARVN. We started with four choppers but one aborted with a "mechanical" caused by contaminated fuel – a persistent problem.

We headed out over flat paddy fields and started toward high ground. My pilot, Lieutenant Leonarduzzi, took us to a hilltop of elephant grass where we laagered overnight – three

Huey crews, plus a Green Beret captain who was to link up with the ARVN and "advise" them.

That night we slept in and under the choppers. Lieutenant Leonarduzzi used a map, known as WAC Chart, to point out an area of marshland where we intended to insert ARVN troops. This would put them behind a Viet Cong force retiring to the north and they would be able to set up an ambush.

Teddy Knapp had wandered over from his helicopter. "Sir, I think some Cong are running around in the low area over there." He pointed into the pitch black. "They must know we're coming."

"Naw," said the captain. "They're not this close."

That night we heard small-arms fire in the distance, and again before dawn. "Somebody's gettin' shot up out there," said my co-pilot, CWO Olsen. "I wonder if there's more than one VC unit around here."

Early the next morning, we linked up with a small unit of supposedly fresh, battle-ready ARVN troops. But they looked exhausted, skittish, and downright surly. I sat in on a hasty conference with their officer, the Green Beret captain, and our Huey pilots. The gist was that the ARVN had already skirmished with the VC, and not the same VC unit they were expecting.

"We don't have any other resources," the captain told the ARVN officer. All of us wished we'd had some reconnaissance, some intelligence. "We'll just have to play the situation as we go along."

"We aren't paid for good ideas"

"Sir," I interrupted. "Wouldn't it be a good idea to cancel this operation until we learn more?"

"Yeah, sure," said Leonarduzzi, always the detractor. "And what are you going to do with these ARVNs here? Leave them in suspended animation while we bug out?"

"We aren't paid for good ideas," said the Green Beret, who looked like he ought to be carrying a knife between his teeth. He nodded toward our chopper, Iron Lady. "Let's saddle up."

We went into the LZ in line-astern formation – Checkers, Iron Lady and El Malo Coolo, three Hueys packed with ARVN troops, rushing across paddy fields and marshes. I got myself into a comfortable position to lean over the M60 and keep the machine-guns trained at a quarter-angle to the front. The noise and windblast were terrific.

Suddenly, a couple of tracers whipped past in front of us. Then a couple more. The intercom was rigged to the radio and I heard Checkers' pilot say, "We're hit."

"****," somebody said.

"They got a hydraulic line. There's oil shooting everywhere."

"Christ, Teddy's been hit! He's bleeding all over the place!"

"I'm hurtin'," came Teddy's own voice.

I watched the UH-1B swerve off to our right, pieces of debris falling back behind it, and remembered Teddy's prediction that he was going to come back dead. I depressed the M60 and fired some rounds. I saw water and mud being kicked up by our gunfire and it looked like we'd hit one of them. But I also heard the crunching sound of our Iron Lady being hit.

We were lucky. Leonarduzzi took us upstairs and the UH-1B seemed to be flying okay. Our ARVN passengers were scared, chattering and gesturing wildly, uncertain what was going on.

"Let's get out of here!"

Teddy Knapp's helicopter moved away over the paddy fields with a thin streak of black jetting back from it. "I've got control," the pilot said. "But we gotta make a decision here."

"That's just a handful of VC," interjected the Green Berets' answer to John Wayne. "Leave 'em. Leave 'em. We gotta move on down to insert these friendlies."

"I think I can stay with you," Checkers reported. I imagined Teddy hanging on to his M60 for dear life while the chopper slewed and bumped its way through the sky.

"Okay," said Lieutenant Leonarduzzi. "It's up beyond that hill. Ten o'clock, to the west. We'll put 'em in there."

We set down in foot-deep water with little green rice sprouts protruding above the surface – now several miles from where we'd been fired on – and our ARVN troops went storming and splashing out of the choppers. It was great to be rid of the load, and we were not sorry to see the gung-ho Special Forces captain leave with them.

"Bye-bye time," shouted El Malo Coolo's pilot. "Let's get out of here!"

Our mission was over, I told myself. It would be nice to have a cold beer when we got home.

I was leaning against my harness, part of my body poking out into the slipstream, play-acting with the M60 ("rat-tat-tat") and thinking about that beer when we flew directly over a column of 250 North Vietnamese regular infantrymen.

An American 'adviser' leads a South Vietnamese machine-gun team. The gun is a Browning .30-cal and the rifles are World War II M1 carbines.

TUNNEL WARFARE

A US soldier clutching a Colt .45 takes part in tunnel clearing operations in the Ho Bo Woods during the Vietnam war. The Vietnamese earth was particularly suitable for tunnelling: it allowed water to drain away while remaining very hard. Extensive tunnel systems were built; they have now been enlarged for use as a tourist attraction.

For 63 days — from 1 August to 2 October, 1944 — Warsaw was ablaze as the Polish Underground Army (AK) fought the German army from house to house, basement to basement, and sewer to sewer.

The success of the AK against the might of the Wehrmacht and elements of the SS was a direct result of their extensive use of sewers – urban tunnels! Twenty-two years later in South Vietnam, elements of the 1st US Infantry Division, the Big Red One, went into action against the Viet Cong, who fought them from an extensive system of tunnels that criss-crossed under the Ho Bo Woods close to Saigon in Cu Chi District.

The first task of any force operating from tunnels or sewers is to establish a detailed knowledge of the area so that they can move from one area to another. The VC built their tunnels to cover vast areas, and the soldiers who lived and fought in them knew their areas intimately. The VC doctrine for the use of tunnels stressed that combat had absolute priority and shelter came second. Underneath the ground were hospitals, workshops for the making of home-made mines and bombs, operating theatres and even graveyards. Likewise, in Warsaw, the underground fighters of the AK knew the labyrinth of sewers and tunnels that ran beneath their city. When fighters had to move from one sector to another, they would be guided by local personnel from that area.

Living constantly underground requires great toughness and discipline. It is dark, the air is hot and foetid, the area cramped and claustrophobic, and always there is the constant fear of being trapped and buried beneath tons of soil. People living in tunnels sweat constantly, and any activity causes laboured breathing.

Urban tunnels

Tunnel warfare is a most effective method of fighting and not necessarily an outdated one: it is a likely scenario for any future European war. Forces in tunnels engage the enemy from areas they considered safe. Once alerted, the enemy move to the area from where they received fire and set off booby traps hidden in the grass or

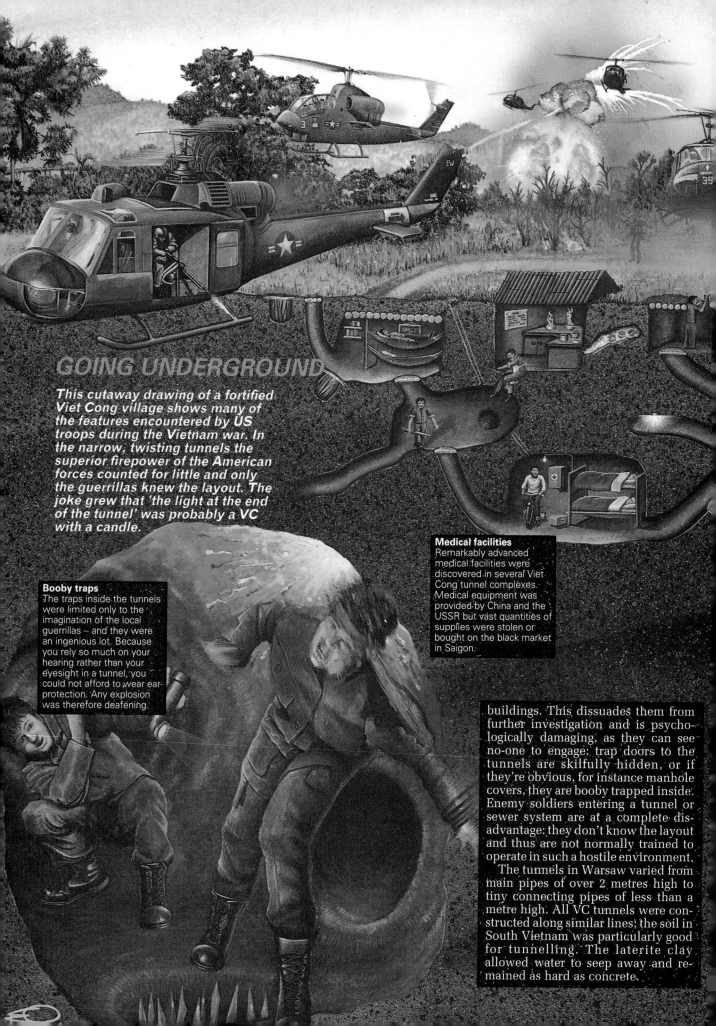

GOING UNDERGROUND

This cutaway drawing of a fortified Viet Cong village shows many of the features encountered by US troops during the Vietnam war. In the narrow, twisting tunnels the superior firepower of the American forces counted for little and only the guerrillas knew the layout. The joke grew that 'the light at the end of the tunnel' was probably a VC with a candle.

Medical facilities
Remarkably advanced medical facilities were discovered in several Viet Cong tunnel complexes. Medical equipment was provided by China and the USSR but vast quantities of supplies were stolen or bought on the black market in Saigon.

Booby traps
The traps inside the tunnels were limited only to the imagination of the local guerrillas — and they were an ingenious lot. Because you rely so much on your hearing rather than your eyesight in a tunnel, you could not afford to wear ear-protection. Any explosion was therefore deafening.

buildings. This dissuades them from further investigation and is psychologically damaging, as they can see no-one to engage: trap doors to the tunnels are skilfully hidden, or if they're obvious, for instance manhole covers, they are booby trapped inside. Enemy soldiers entering a tunnel or sewer system are at a complete disadvantage: they don't know the layout and thus are not normally trained to operate in such a hostile environment.

The tunnels in Warsaw varied from main pipes of over 2 metres high to tiny connecting pipes of less than a metre high. All VC tunnels were constructed along similar lines; the soil in South Vietnam was particularly good for tunnelling. The laterite clay allowed water to seep away and remained as hard as concrete.

Ventilation
Although narrow, sloping ventilation tunnels were added as frequently as possible, the tunnels were still very hot.

Tunnel security
The Viet Cong only occupied tunnel complexes when they could no longer live in relative safety in the villages. As US forces extended their grip over the countryside near Saigon, so the VC were forced underground. The scale of their diggings around Chu Chi never became fully known until after the war.

Tunnel layout
By constructing several levels of tunnels and concealing the connecting passageways the Viet Cong could hope to survive even if the complex was overrun by US forces. So long as the full extent of the tunnels was not discovered and their final hiding places were not gassed or filled in, the guerrillas could emerge when the US forces eventually left the area.

Stores
The quantity of hardware found in some tunnels beggared belief. One complex overrun by American troops even included an M48 tank, taken by the Viet Cong in an earlier battle and buried in their underground base.

Underwater entrance
An underwater entrance like this was inconvenient to use regularly but hard for the enemy to find. Weapons caches were often stored in caves excavated under overhanging river banks.

The tunnels were designed for fighting inside, but also allowed escape through secret passages. They were not straight, but constantly twisted with corners between 60° and 120°: these zigzags were for strength and also to deflect explosive blasts and long-range shooting.

Trapdoor system

A clever and finely engineered trapdoor system was devised, creating entrances and exits from one level to another. These trapdoors were invisible and could stand the weight of a man or an armoured vehicle. The hundreds of tons of earth taken from the tunnels were concealed with great care: hidden under houses, poured into streams, scattered, but never left in piles where they could be seen from the air. Enormous B-52 bomb craters were frequently used to dump fresh spoil.

Inside the tunnels, a drainage hole was dug every 20 metres to prevent flooding in the annual monsoons. Also, every 30 metres or so, water traps were built; these stopped the entry of toxic gases and fumes into other parts of the tunnel. In this way, parts of the complex could be effectively sealed off whenever smoke or gas was pumped in to try to force out the inhabitants.

Attacking sewers and underground pipes is a little easier in FIBUA combat. First of all, the attacker can generally obtain maps of the underground systems and plan more effective assaults. Secondly, urban sewers and tunnels are bigger than hand-made tunnels, so movement is a little easier. Also, tunnel lengths are longer, so there are fewer opportunities for the close in ambush so prevalent in VC tunnel fighting – the spear in the throat or the shot in the groin as a tunnel searcher enters a tunnel or changes from one level to another.

In Warsaw, the Germans, with teutonic thoroughness, sectioned off each area and then poured petrol into the sewers and ignited it to destroy the oxygen, or pumped in smoke. This was followed by the assault teams, who moved using fire and movement, clearing pipes section by section. Progress was reported to the surface and troops were stationed at the entrances and manholes to stop anyone escaping.

Although progress was slow and

Explosives are lowered into the tunnel complex to destroy it. Many methods were tried, including pumping in gasoline and burning them out. CS gas was also tried but the Viet Cong defeated this by building water-filled sumps to block the passage of the gas.

the Germans sustained many casualties, the extent of each complex was known and so the tunnel fighters' areas were slowly whittled away. The episode had, however, shown the successful use of sewers and tunnels in a bitterly fought urban battle.

The tunnel war against the VC was a different affair and not as successful. The Americans fighting the VC in their own tunnels sent in their own trained 'tunnel rats' to find the VC in the merciless maze of diggings: these tunnel rats were called forward whenever major tunnel complexes were found.

These volunteers were a special breed of soldier. Normally small and wiry, they were men who could work alone in the dark subterranean world beneath the feet and tank-tracks of their colleagues. Dressed in combat fatigues, jungle boots and carrying a knife, pistol and torch, the rats would descend in teams into the tunnels. They had perfected their own techniques in 'safe' tunnels, learning to move lying on their stomachs, holding the torch and pistol, and crawling without making any noise or disturbing the earth.

Respirators needed

They often had to wear gas masks to protect themselves against the gas and CS that lingered after attacks. Firing weapons in the close confines of a tunnel was deafening, but the rats could not afford to wear ear defenders because they needed to hear every sound.

Silencers on pistols were not used because they made the weapon too long and cumbersome. The bayonet and the fighting knife became the tun-

VIET CONG DEFENCES

These diagrams show actual types of position encountered by US forces in Vietnam.

The entrance to the hidden bunker is concealed beneath the hearth of the hut. This sort of dug-out was often used by communist cadres living semi-openly in villages.

Viet Cong tunnel entrances were sometimes protected by booby-traps, mines, or firing positions. Since it took enormous effort to stockpile military equipment in their bases, the Viet Cong were often prepared to fight hard to stop US forces finding them.

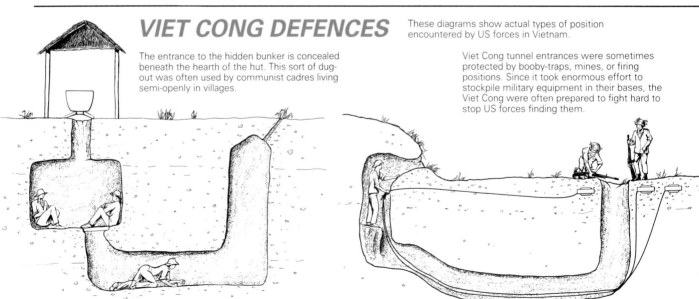

used in the tunnels, but they tended to set off booby traps.

Tunnel warfare incorporates all the normal phases of war – attack, defence and withdrawal – but is fought under circumstances that favour the defender. The defender's local knowledge of the sewers of a city or the tunnels in a jungle mean that the attacker is always at a disadvantage. The size and firepower of a large army is of little value in the dark, frightening, one-on-one battle below the ground.

An attacker can only be successful in tunnel warfare if every operation is based on good intelligence using all the maps and captured information available. The soldiers chosen to fight underground must be selected from strongly disciplined troops who can operate in extreme conditions. The equipment carried in tunnel warfare is minimal; heavy weapons and grenades are dangerous to both sides. Hand to hand combat is quite common. Night-vision goggles give a great advantage, avoiding the use of illumination and white light. Communication is difficult, but some form of recognition is essential to avoid unnecessary casualties.

Tunnel warfare is one of the coldest and most frightening forms of combat, and if troops are to succeed in the underground battle they must be tough, well-disciplined and, most important of all, highly motivated.

The Viet Cong tunnels were cramped even for the small-statured Vietnamese and caused serious problems for the US troops. Underground navigation was very difficult: smoke was sometimes pumped down to reveal other entrances to the complex.

nel rat's best pieces of equipment; they were used as probes for trap doors and booby traps or as close combat weapons. The rats did not use communications because radios were ineffective and cumbersome. This lack of communication with the surface sometimes caused unnecessary casualties, when tunnel rats would emerge on the surface near soldiers who were not expecting them.

In Warsaw, too, there were frequent clashes in the underground world as Germans or AKs shot each other by mistake. In the dark half-world of the sewer and tunnel, the policy had to be shoot or stab first and ask questions afterwards. Dogs were sometimes

Viet Cong fighting positions were sometimes linked underground, enabling small numbers of guerrillas to tie down major forces. As they moved rapidly between bunkers it was very difficult to determine their true strength or deployment.

Two riverbank dug-outs: a room-sized storage facility and a one-man 'Spider Hole' (a popular Viet Cong defensive position). The thick vegetation along the waterways in the Mekong Delta provided excellent cover for concealed positions.

Traps built into tunnel systems accounted for many US troops listed as MIA (Missing In Action) since their bodies were never recovered. Here, the tunnel entrance drops into a punji stake pit covered by two riflemen.

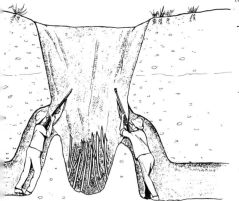

Spear-armed Viet Cong killed several tunnel rats using variations of this technique. Some were double ambushes: the first soldier into the tunnel is stabbed and the men attempting to rescue him receive a grenade posted into the tunnel entrance by the Viet Cong.

Combat Report
Vietnam:
Helicopter Engagement Part 2

Mike Greenwood continues his story of an engagement between Huey helicopters and a huge NVA infantry force in Vietnam in 1964.

One moment, I was looking at low hillocks and flooded paddies. The next, I was gazing directly at the largest communist force seen by Americans up to this point. They were stocky little men in green-brown fatigues, moving deftly and with a discipline like nothing we'd ever seen. I reached for the intercom switch but the lieutenant beat me to it. "Over to the right are all the gooks in the world!"

"My God!" Olson chimed in. "It's the whole humping North Vietnamese army!"

I was supposed to await instructions but I didn't. I aligned the pip, and pulled the trigger. Simultaneously, I was thrown violently to the right and would have gone flying out of the aircraft had my harness not restrained me. I had a glimpse of my burst hitting the NVA and I heard Leonarduzzi: "We're gonna engage."

"Right behind you," said El Malo Coolo.

"Get to their rear! Get behind them! Those bastards have twelve point sevens!" — meaning 12.7-mm heavy machine guns.

The NVA were scattering

"Be advised Checkers has a wounded man on board." This was not exactly big news. "We'll stick with you for the moment, but –"

The breath was pushed from my lungs. I was hanging in space. Goddamned Leonarduzzi had thrown the UH-1B into a violent turn without warning me! When I worked myself back into the doorway behind the gun – gasping and struggling to get hold of myself – the chopper turned so that I could not bring the gun to bear. "Back to the right!" I shouted angrily to Leonarduzzi. The NVA were scattering. I caught the red-orange of their muzzle flashes.

The airwaves were filled with voices as the pilots of Checkers, Iron Lady, and El Malo Coolo all thought of the same thing at once – help! We didn't have much in the way of command and control, and it took some confusion and a lot of shouting before what the pilots already knew was confirmed: no other friendly aircraft were anywhere in the region.

The three Hueys were swinging back and forth like insects over the NVA, trying to dodge NVA fire and get us door gunners into position

to do some damage. Despite their obvious professionalism, the NVA were surprised by our arrival and apparently had no plan to cope with helicopters. We made a very low pass just parallel to the NVA column. I had a stark, close-up view of them prone in defensive positions, trying to shoot back. I fired short, careful bursts, following an imaginary line that ran along them. I could see the bullets hitting. I actually saw one man take hits in the back and buttocks, contort violently for an instant, and become limp.

El Malo Coolo took hits. Later we learned that bullets shattered the windshield, spraying pilot and co-pilot with shards of glass, and that bullet fragments hit the co-pilot in the shoulder and neck, causing massive bleeding. "We're gettin' out!" shouted the pilot, who was technically the flight leader. "Leonarduzzi, you got the helm."

Lieutenant Leonarduzzi faced a painful decision. We were terribly low on fuel and had no idea of Teddy Knapp's condition aboard Checkers. We had achieved what the ARVN troops hadn't – pinned down a major enemy force (some records say that these were the first North Vietnamese regulars ever engaged in the conflict) – and we were inflicting real harm. With the worst-hit Huey now a shrinking silhouette on the horizon, Leonarduzzi radioed Checkers' pilot.

"Let's do one more firing pass, opposite directions, zigzag, and get as many of them as we can. Then we head for –" he gave the code word for a laager point where we could refuel. "One pass, make it count."

The last pass

"Lieutenant," I said, "Parallel again, but this time lean into them. Give me a few degrees of bank."

"Aim to please," he shot back.

I could feel the adrenalin churning inside. "I'll get some of 'em, don't you worry . . ."

The two pilots orchestrated it with flawless synchronization – banking, turning, and coming out of the turn face-to-face in perfect unison. The two UH-1Bs rushed at each other as if bent on a collision, Teddy and me firing from the right side of each craft. All of us subconsciously arranged this so that our own fire would not endanger each other.

As we made that ultimate firing pass, I saw muzzle flashes and tracers all around us. I felt

the pilots' heavy breathing in my earphones. I looked at the North Vietnamese – almost close enough to see the whites of their eyes, as they said at Bunker Hill – and I know damn well that some of them were just as scared of us as we were of them.

We were not expected to return to pick up the ARVN troops and we didn't. But we heard later that they never came into contact with any of the three enemy components in the area – the Viet Cong guerrillas they'd known were present, the Viet Cong we'd discovered, and the dramatic-sized force of NVA.

Our tactics were changed

In those days, the ARVN were widely understood to be willing to fight only if there was no chance of being hurt – in a much-publicised incident at the time, ARVN soldiers stood at the edge of a treeline and watched US adviser Captain Kenneth Good die of wounds, rather than risk VC gunfire – but whatever their faults, they didn't compare with those of the American top brass who'd decided that helicopter assaults could be carried out in small numbers. Our tactics were quickly changed (no one was happier about it than the major, our company CO), and after that, all helicopter insertions required the participation of at least a dozen Hueys, including gunships.

We may have been the first example of that Vietnam charade known as the "body count". Somebody in Saigon, who hadn't seen any bodies or done any counting, officially credited us with 37 enemy killed, after altering the facts to make it appear we'd been supporting an ARVN action rather than operating alone. Casualty figures are usually inflated but I believe we really did despatch at least that many NVA.

Teddy had scared the hell out of his crew – his blood was everywhere – but although briefly unconscious on the way home, he had only minor wounds. Teddy's premonition about dying because of our questionable helicopter tactics was like many other ideas we had during those years: wrong.

Left: A flight of UH-1D 'slicks' near Pleiku. Once US ground troops entered the war, airmobile techniques were developed rapidly and helicopter armament was uprated. Below: A column of Viet Cong march through Vietnam. In 1964 they were beginning to mount large-scale conventional ops.

DEPLOYING THE CLAYMORE

9 TIPS FOR USING CLAYMORES

1. Always camouflage the bandolier for the mine so that you can use it to conceal and protect the mine once you have set it up.
2. Camouflage the detonator cord and bury all wires.
3. Do not loop the firing wire round the legs of the mine: someone will walk into it and pull the mine over. Secure it to a stake driven into the ground.
4. Do not dig up or pull up foliage near the mine.
5. Always use a dual initiation circuit, i.e. a blasting cap in both detonator wells and two separate circuits.
6. Do not put Claymores in front of trees: they have a nasty habit of crashing down when you fire the mine.
7. Make sure that the cut-off groups in the ambush position can also fire the Claymores if they are bounced by the enemy.
8. Do not transmit radio messages near armed Claymores; they can set the mines off! ("Random frequency hazard").
9. Make sure you are behind some solid cover and at least 16 m behind or to the side of a mine. You must be able to see all your mines from this position.

The Claymore was used widely in Vietnam as a perimeter defence weapon and in ambush tasks. Why stick your head up in an ambush position to fire a rifle when you can do it 700 times better with fragmentation and ball bearings from a Claymore?

Claymore mines can be used for ambushing, defending bases, and when withdrawing. But it is in the ambush that the Claymore mine has made the greatest impact, particularly in close country. It can cover a killing area with instantaneous firepower, reducing the number of soldiers you need. It can also be used either to supplement the small-arms fire in a conventional ambush or as the principal weapon in a "mechanical" ambush.

Effective firepower

The main advantage of using the Claymore in your ambush is that it provides a degree of firepower out of all proportion to the size of the patrol and, unlike small-arms fire, there is no tendency to shoot high at night. It also makes your ambush less easy to detect. Even the most disciplined soldiers, having been in the jungle for some days, will accumulate smells, make noises, move and become less alert. The Claymore mine does none of these.

The system does of course have its disadvantages. The mines take time to

Combat Skills

The Soviets have produced their own Claymore. In a war in Europe the enemy would be active throughout the depth of NATO's defences, so you cannot afford to move like this (left); good spacing will minimise casualties (right).

set up and, if you have not used them, time to dismantle. If you have to get out, you may have to abandon them. Once sited, they can only fire into that arc. Also, the Claymore is a one-shot

THE MECHANICAL AMBUSH

Recent advances in the efficiency of unmanned ground sensors (UGS) means the potential of the Claymore has been considerably enhanced. Groups of Claymores can be deployed with UGS on known guerrilla infiltration routes and monitored and initiated from a safe area. This may not be as efficient as deploying troops on the ground to mop up the survivors, but it involves very little effort and risk to the security forces. When an ambush is fired after enemy movement is detected, a quick reaction force can be sent out from the defended area to follow up the mechanical ambush. Further casualties may be inflicted on the enemy by careful booby-trapping of the bodies and equipment.

Booby traps
In Vietnam, mines left protecting defended localities were stolen in vast quantities by the Viet Cong and used against their former owners. The only real way to stop this happening is by observation and direct fire. In this situation you can discourage the practice by wiring mines up to a secondary mine or booby trap as an anti-handling device.

Body searching
Do not place the mines on the track you are ambushing. If the mines are too close on firing, bodies are propelled through the trees, which makes body searching difficult.

Infra-red systems
These usually involve the target breaking a beam between two sensors which register on a set. By looking at where the beams have been broken on your sketch map you may be able to tell whether the target is human and even what patrol formation they are using. But be careful: infra-red beams can be seen by an enemy using infra-red goggles.

Hazards
Do not fire a mine that is dislodged from its intended position or has fallen over. The results can be highly unpredictable and a hazard to your own troops.

Multiple mine ambush
Use the mines laid out in two banks, fired simultaneously to give crossfire coverage of the killing zone for best effect. Each mine is connected via det cord so that the mines will fire simultaneously with a detonator in each well of an individual mine.

Shock effect
Claymores have considerable shock effect and can be used as part of a 'break contact' drill for a patrol caught up in a fire fight it does not look like winning. A short fuzed Claymore plonked down in the path of an advancing enemy while you disappear rapidly in the other direction is a very effective method of breaking clean. However, the drill must be carefully practised beforehand as the scope for disaster is enormous.

Mine destruction
Mines that do not go off should be treated as blinds and destroyed with a demolition charge without touching the mine.

Firing
The mine can be fired electrically or manually by using a blasting cap, det cord and safety fuse. The mine can be set up as a booby trap using either of these initiation methods.

weapon, so not as effective as small-arms when a determined enemy continues to attack.

Many of these disadvantages can be overcome if you are clever when siting your Claymores. The normal ambush position in close country has, as its killing area, a linear feature such as a track, a stream, or the edge of vegetation. In any case, always draw a diagram of the site in order to work out the best configuration of Claymores. Remember, casualty zones and danger areas may be reduced by vegetation. Also, a pack or other equipment may offer some protection. The best protection of all is body armour. You should also take into account the rear blast area of a Claymore. This has a radius of 16 metres, which can be considerably reduced if you site your killer group behind a large tree or in a depression.

Claymores can be used in groups or banks, where simultaneous detonation is initiated from one point. The first mine is detonated by the issued firing device and detonator assembly.

The succeeding mines are detonated by linking them with detonating cord, which has non-electrical detonators at each end; these are then placed in the unused detonator wells of each mine. This is a very effective and reliable method, but it takes time: the detonating cord must be well camouflaged and checked regularly to ensure there is no damage from moisture and fraying.

You can either set your Claymores up in a straight line running parallel to the killing area, or you can achieve a crossfire effect by angling your mines at 45° to the killing area from both your left and right. Another variation is to lay the mines parallel to the killing area to produce an overlap or tissue effect. This configuration is particularly suitable on a long, gradual bend.

Siting the Claymore carefully is very important. Aim low rather than high and, remember, in most circumstances you will not be able to lie down behind the mine to sight it as this will disturb too much undergrowth.

Vulnerability
The sensors should give you an idea of the size of enemy force in your ambush area; even so, the effectiveness of the ambush cannot be exactly predicted. The quick reaction force will be very vulnerable when clearing the ambush position, this should be done with extreme caution.

Mine danger area
Ideally you should be able to see the entire mine danger area, so there is no risk of you firing on the enemy and zapping a friendly patrol as well.

Maintenance
Claymores deployed on a defensive perimeter must be regularly checked for damage and circuit tested. Try to keep out the damp by covering in plastic and taping it down.

Booby trapping the dead
The enemy will try to kill you in any way he can. You must do all you can to inflict casualties and destroy his will to win. The Claymore, correctly used in an ambush, will have a devastating effect. You may be able to inflict further casualties by wiring up equipment and bodies in the ambush area to more concealed Claymores.

Trees
The mine is very effective, if it is correctly sited in trees, where it has an enhanced fragmentation effect.

Ground radar
Skilled operators can distinguish human movement from that of animals. In addition there is a wide range of thermal imaging and noise sensors to warn of enemy approach.

Sensors
Ground sensors detect impacts of feet, tyres or tracks on the ground. Once buried these systems take a while to settle in and can be triggered by animals. It is better to use more than one system to build up an intelligence picture of the target before you fire the ambush and blast a bush pig into orbit.

Testing
When testing the mine, in bright sunlight, hold the test set up against the eye to see the light flash in the window of the test set. Do the same at night so you don't advertise your position.

Random frequency hazard
Radio transmissions near an armed Claymore on an electrical firing circuit may fire the mine. If you are going to use the mines for perimeter defence for a harbour area or permanent base with a heavy volume of radio traffic, it is worth using non-electric initiation using pull wires and det cord.

THE M18A1 CLAYMORE ANTI-PERSONNEL MINE

The Claymore is a directional fixed fragmentation mine primarily for anti-personnel use, and is also effective against thin-skinned vehicles. Fragments will readily perforate the outer body, injuring or killing the occupants. Fragments will also puncture tyres, petrol tanks, crank cases and radiators. When detonated, a fan-shaped pattern of spherical steel fragments is projected over a 60-degree horizontal arc, covering a casualty area of 50m at a height of two meters.

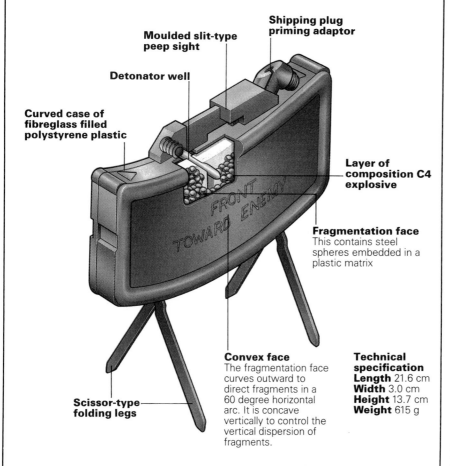

Moulded slit-type peep sight

Shipping plug priming adaptor

Detonator well

Curved case of fibreglass filled polystyrene plastic

FRONT TOWARD ENEMY

Layer of composition C4 explosive

Fragmentation face
This contains steel spheres embedded in a plastic matrix

Convex face
The fragmentation face curves outward to direct fragments in a 60 degree horizontal arc. It is concave vertically to control the vertical dispersion of fragments.

Scissor-type folding legs

Technical specification
Length 21.6 cm
Width 3.0 cm
Height 13.7 cm
Weight 615 g

Priming the mine: insert into the detonator well into the electric blasting cap, which is connected to 30m of firing wire. Attached to the firing wire connector is a shorting plug which prevents the blasting cap being fired by a build-up of static electricity.

Claymores are also effective when used in the defence of a platoon, company or battalion jungle base. Site the mine outside the perimeter, or in areas of "dead" ground that might be difficult to cover with small-arms fire. Wherever possible, Claymores should be covered by aimed fire. If your enemy has been checked by a detonated mine, your defence will be much more effective if you immediately engage him with aimed fire: he will not have time to recover.

Early warning devices

You will know when to detonate your Claymores if you site early warning devices or Unattended Ground Sensors (UGS) with them. During the Vietnam War, the Viet Cong used to crawl undetected into the outer defences of bases and turn the mines around. Effective UGS and sentries, using modern night surveillance equipment, should be able to prevent this. The most important thing to remember is that Claymores will not work if left out for a long time unchecked. Check them daily, and use a dual firing circuit to ensure detonation.

Claymores can also be used to protect overnight or long-term patrol bases. If the patrol base is merely an overnight stop, then only a few Claymores can be deployed; site them on the perimeter and along likely enemy approaches. They are best initiated from your section sentry position. If you are attacked by a larger force, they might provide the breathing-space you need to escape. A minimum of six Claymores can provide rudimentary all-round cover, but it is, of course, possible to achieve more comprehensive coverage for a patrol base that you might be using as a launching pad for other patrols, and which you would occupy continuously.

Use in withdrawal

As has already been suggested, you can use Claymores in the withdrawal. Prepare the mine with a non-electrical detonator fitted with a short length of safety fuse, and have it facing the enemy. When making your getaway, ignite the safety fuse. Even the most determined enemy follow-up will be delayed by the subsequent detonation.

Whether used as part of an ambush, in defence of bases or when withdrawing, the Claymore mine is a very effective weapon and can be used in any terrain. But if it's not used properly it can be as lethal to your own men as it is to the enemy.

THE CLAYMORE TESTING CIRCUIT

Circuit testing for electrical firing of the mine is recommended but not essential. Before testing always make sure the firing device bail is in the safe position.

Test procedure

1 First test the firing device by attaching the test set and pressing the actuator.
2 Then test the whole circuit by plugging in the firing wire connected to the blasting wire.
3 A light in the test set window indicates the circuit is OK.

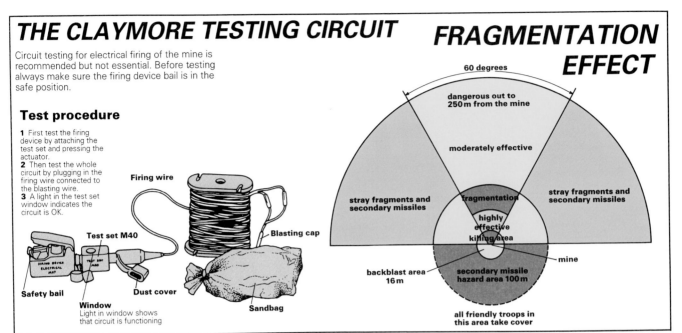

Firing wire

Blasting cap

Test set M40

Safety bail

Dust cover

Sandbag

Window
Light in window shows that circuit is functioning

FRAGMENTATION EFFECT

60 degrees

dangerous out to 250 m from the mine

moderately effective

stray fragments and secondary missiles

fragmentation

highly effective killing area

stray fragments and secondary missiles

mine

backblast area 16 m

secondary missile hazard area 100 m

all friendly troops in this area take cover

HOW TO SET UP THE MINE

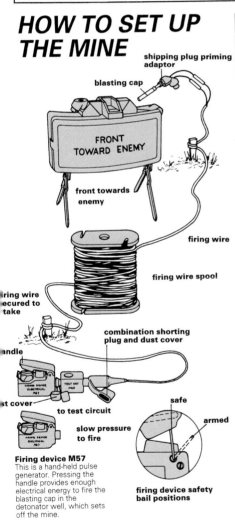

shipping plug priming adaptor

blasting cap

FRONT TOWARD ENEMY

front towards enemy

firing wire

firing wire spool

firing wire secured to take

handle

combination shorting plug and dust cover

dust cover

to test circuit

safe

armed

slow pressure to fire

firing device safety bail positions

Firing device M57
This is a hand-held pulse generator. Pressing the handle provides enough electrical energy to fire the blasting cap in the detonator well, which sets off the mine.

The mine is issued in a bag-type bandolier containing all you need to set up, test and fire the mine. The mine circuit shown above has the test set in position. Simply remove the test set from the firing wire and replace with the firing circuit, then place the blasting cap in the detonator well.

CORRECT SIGHTING PROCEDURE AND DANGER AREAS

100 m to the rear and sides of the mine, all troops must take cover

16 m safe firing distance if under cover.

alternative aiming points

aiming point

eye

mine

line of sight

1.5 m

1.8 m

2.4 m

slit trench

slit-type peep sight

15 m

30 m

45 m

sight picture through the peep sight

aiming point

groove

2 m

fragmentation area

50 m

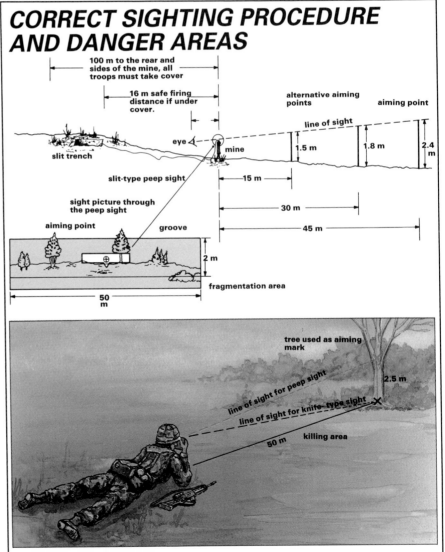

tree used as aiming mark

2.5 m

line of sight for peep sight

line of sight for knife-type sight

50 m

killing area

There are two types of Claymore currently manufactured, one with a peep sight, where the point of aim at 50 m is about 2.5 m above the ground, and a knifeblade-type sight where the aiming point at 50 m is ground level.

Battle Fitness Programme No. 13

CIRCUIT TRAINING TECHNIQUES

Circuit training is an excellent method of getting fit in the shortest possible time. It is used a great deal in the British armed forces, and is especially useful for training large groups of men or where training facilities are restricted, for example on board ship or in Northern Ireland locations.

A circuit is a set of exercises done in succession, without a pause. Each exercise is performed a predetermined number of times ('repetitions'). As each participant becomes fitter, he progresses to a second, or even third, circuit. Each exercise has a target, for general or muscle-specific endurance.

An effective circuit

To be fully effective, a circuit must fulfil the following requirements:

1 The exercises, number of repetitions and rate of progress should be based upon each individual's capacity for work.

2 It must apply the 'overload principle': when a muscle can contract comfortably against a resistance, that resistance must be increased.

3 The exercises used should be simple, but strenuous enough to contribute to the overall workload.

4 All the body's muscles must be exercised.

5 No single group of muscles should be exercised continuously.

6 The circuit should not contain fewer than eight or more than 10 exercises.

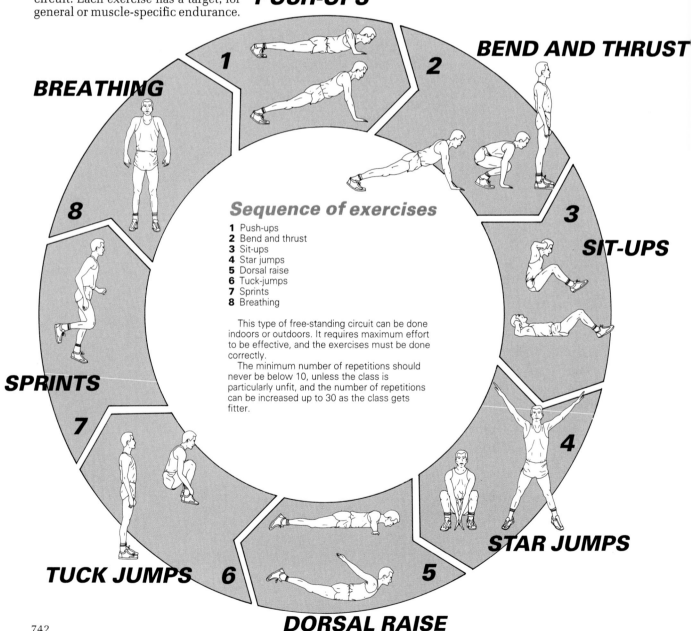

PUSH-UPS 1

BEND AND THRUST 2

BREATHING 8

SIT-UPS 3

SPRINTS 7

STAR JUMPS 4

TUCK JUMPS 6

DORSAL RAISE 5

Sequence of exercises

1 Push-ups
2 Bend and thrust
3 Sit-ups
4 Star jumps
5 Dorsal raise
6 Tuck-jumps
7 Sprints
8 Breathing

This type of free-standing circuit can be done indoors or outdoors. It requires maximum effort to be effective, and the exercises must be done correctly.

The minimum number of repetitions should never be below 10, unless the class is particularly unfit, and the number of repetitions can be increased up to 30 as the class gets fitter.

Free-standing circuit

A commonly-used form of circuit is the Free-Standing Circuit, which requires no equipment. It takes about 20 minutes, and each exercise is usually repeated 10-15 times.

Everyone must be thoroughly warmed up beforehand. The group runs in a circle with three to five metre intervals between each person. After three or four laps, the leader specifies an exercise and stipulates the number of repetitions to the class (or he can demonstrate the exercises inside the circle).

On the word 'go' the group stops running, faces the centre and completes the exercise as instructed. When each participant finishes his repetitions, he continues to run in the circle. When the whole group has completed the exercises and is running again the next exercise is called, and so on – until all the exercises have been completed. Breathing exercises may be allowed between circuits.

In group circuit training you start running around the circuit as soon as you have finished the correct number of repetitions of the exercise. Once everyone has finished and is running in a circle you can move on to the next exercise.

The individual circuit

You can use the Free-Standing Circuit to train on your own, and will find it even more effective if you carry out your exercises around a measured course of up to one mile in distance. This allows plenty of cardiovascular training between exercise stations, especially when you get fit enough to complete three circuits: this would allow a maximum training effect in a minimum amount of time.

Below: American servicemen demonstrate free-standing circuit training. This is most effective as a group training method, but you can use it as an individual.

The Tuck Jump
From a standing position, jump up and tuck your arms around your shins. After plenty of practice you should be able to get up to this sort of height.

HOW TO START A JOGGING PROGRAMME

Millions of people all over the world jog every day. Jogging has been defined as running a mile in more than nine minutes, while running means doing a mile in under nine minutes. It is cheap, convenient, relieves stress, gives a great deal of cardiovascular benefit for the time expended – and you don't need any lessons.

You don't need to run long distances, either. About 15 miles per week will give maximum fitness.

Planning your programme

Don't do too much too soon, or you will hurt yourself. Follow these guidelines:

1 Frequency

To start with, try 2-3 jogging sessions per week. After about 10 weeks you may feel fit enough to increase this to 4-5 times per week (which is great for weight loss). The physiological returns on training every day are just not worth the extra effort.

2 Intensity

To start with, train at 60 per cent of your maximum heart rate, increasing this to 70 per cent when you feel ready and 85 per cent when you get to peak fitness.

3 Duration

Initially you may only be able to work at your target heart rate for 5-10 minutes. In order to get a good training effect, however, you need to be able to jog for 20-30 minutes per session. This can increase to 45-60 minutes when you are at peak fitness.

4 Type of activity

It is not necessary to stick to the same route – variety is the spice of life! Try to find soft tracks or grassy banks to absorb shock. By using various routes you will prevent boredom. As you get fitter you can tackle hills to provide more variety.

US Marines running as part of their fitness programme. Regular jogging is the most cost-effective exercise you can take: you need little equipment, no gym facilities, and no instructions.

Like any other aerobic exercise, jogging will:

* improve heart and lung efficiency
* strengthen muscles, bones and connective tissue
* improve oxygen use in blood cells
* help control high blood pressure
* lower body fat and cholesterol
* rid the body of poisonous toxins and waste

There is no better way of getting and staying fit than regular jogging. Once you get into the habit you will be surprised how enjoyable it becomes: it will soon be an indispensable part of your daily life.

Jogging style

This is very important and should be constantly checked. The correct style will prevent over-use injuries.

1 Relax all muscles that are not directly involved in the running action. If you tense the muscles in your arms, neck and shoulders it will increase fatigue and cause an energy drain.

2 Hold your head comfortably: not tilted either too far forward or too far back, and not moving from side to side. Keep it as still as possible, looking about 10 metres ahead, to conserve energy.

3 Relax your shoulders and centre them directly over your hips, moving them naturally in co-ordination with your stride.

4 Swing your arms in a relaxed, comfortable motion across your body, with your hands loosely cupped.

5 Plant your feet in a natural, rolling movement from your heel to the ball of your foot, so that the final push comes from your toes.

A jogging machine allows you to monitor and regulate your exercise. You can also use purpose-built running tracks, which have a special surface designed to reduce foot and ankle strain.

UPPER BODY STRENGTHENING EXERCISES

Climbing, especially with equipment, requires a good deal of upper body strength and local muscular endurance.

Types of exercise

There are many exercises that will help to develop your upper body: here are some that will provide the quickest and best results. Supplement your normal training by selecting 3-5 exercises from the following:

1 Push-ups	dumb-bell press
2 Pull-ups	**7** Bench press
3 Rope climbing	**8** Single arm row
4 Lateral pull-down	**9** Barbell curls
5 Press behind neck	**10** Sit-ups
6 Alternate	

Any exercises selected should be done progressively to the 'point of overload' for maximum benefits.

In all the modern countries of the Western world there is a common weakness — the males have weak upper bodies. Jogging maintains strong legs, but very few people do enough exercise to develop the upper body.

In the military services this can have serious consequences: if you are unable when required to pull yourself, your rifle and your equipment up ropes or over obstacles, you are a liability. So as well as increasing your aerobic fitness through jogging or similar exercise, you should add some regular upper body exercises to your work-out. As well as being stronger, you will also look good!

Push-ups
Keep your head upright. Go all the way down, and lock your arms out on the way up. You can improve your wrist muscles by clenching your fists.

Pull-ups
Your chest should contact the bar and your arms should be fully extended on the down. Use both overhand and underhand grips.

Rope climb
Do not use your legs; this is designed to isolate the upper body muscle groups and improve your grip and endurance.

Lateral pull-down
Avoid banging the weights; control them throughout the movement and do not release them at full extension. Breathe in as you pull the weight down.

Press behind neck: start
Do not bounce or jerk the weight, and make sure you can lift it comfortably. Breathe out as you push up, and in as you lower the weight under control.

Press behind neck: finish
For building tissue use maximum weight and maximum repetitions. You will also have to change your diet!

The muscles
There are many muscles in your upper body, but the most important ones are:

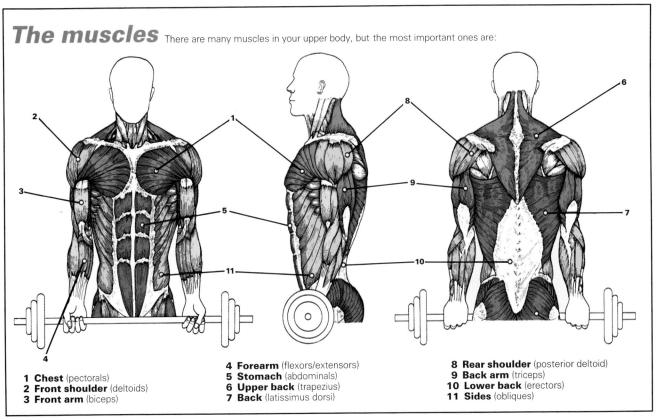

1 Chest (pectorals)
2 Front shoulder (deltoids)
3 Front arm (biceps)

4 Forearm (flexors/extensors)
5 Stomach (abdominals)
6 Upper back (trapezius)
7 Back (latissimus dorsi)

8 Rear shoulder (posterior deltoid)
9 Back arm (triceps)
10 Lower back (erectors)
11 Sides (obliques)

Alternate dumbbell press
If you do not want to build muscle, use a light weight with many repetitions to condition the muscle groups.

Bench press
Breathe out as you push up. Do not bounce the weight off your sternum, as this is damaging. If you are pressing your maximum weight, have someone ready to take the weight off you.

Bench press
To vary the exercise, you can breathe in as you press the weight. Be careful not to do this with too much weight.

Single-arm row
For maximum benefit, do as many repetitions as you can, as fast as possible, in a continuous movement. This is a great help when carrying the SLR in the alert position for long periods.

Barbell curls
Keep the body upright and do not use your back. Breathe in as you raise the bar to your chest.

Sit-ups
You can vary the degree of difficulty by altering the angle of the bench and vary the exercise by twisting the elbows to alternate knees.

747

Holding the Line with Challenger

Challenger is one of the finest main battle tanks in the world, but has one of the strangest of development histories. The cost-conscious British Government never intended to introduce Challenger, preferring instead to equip its armoured regiments with the 900 or so elderly Chieftains either in service or reserve, by cannibalisation if necessary, until the introduction of a radical new tank in the 1990s.

Work on the production of a successor to Chieftain began in the 1960s, developing into a bilateral programme with West Germany, but British and West German priorities were so different that nothing came of it. West Germany went on to develop the highly successful Leopard 2, and Britain returned to the embryonic and purely national MBT-80 programme.

Meanwhile, despite its engine problems, Chieftain was proving popular with several of Britain's non-European allies. The Shah of Iran, then the richest monarch in the non-Arab world, ordered 700 Chieftain Vs for his own army, many of which are seeing service today in the Iran-Iraq War.

Foreign improvement

British arms manufacturers have long operated a so-called 'foreign customer improvement factor' by which weapons issued to the British Army are then developed to a far higher standard, at correspondingly higher cost, and exported. So when in 1974 the Shah requested an improved version of the Chieftain Mk V with a new Rolls-Royce 1200-hp engine, David Brown TN-37 transmission (to give better mobility) and improved electronic fire control equipment, 125 new tanks, designated Shir 1, were manufactured.

Simultaneously, a revolutionary but incredibly expensive new armour type called Chobham Armour (after the location of the Fighting Vehicles Establishment that developed it) was

The British Army has ordered over 400 Challenger tanks to provide the backbone of its armoured force until the next generation of advanced MBTs is ready in the late 1990s. Challenger is a more agile vehicle than the ponderous Chieftain, and its Chobham armour protects it against hollow charge anti-tank weapons such as RPG-7 or AT-3 'Sagger'.

introduced amid a tight veil of secrecy. Britain could not afford a new tank incorporating Chobham Armour, but the Shah had no such financial constraints and immediately ordered 1,225 Shir 2 tanks based on the Shir 1 but with Chobham Armour.

Challengers are armed with the L11A5 120-mm rifled gun, which fires an APDSFS-T round (Armour Piercing Discarding Sabot Fin Stabilized Tracer, or 'fin' for short) with an effective range of over 3,000 metres.

Commander and gunner emerge from the turret. The commander's cupola is fitted with night surveillance and target acquisition sights and he can lay the gun himself. The turret is designed to mount thermal imagers, which will be fitted to all Challengers.

B

Challenger's hydrogas suspension system and good power-to-weight ratio give it a much better cross-country performance than Chieftain, although it is not as agile as Leopard 2 or the M1 Abrams.

When the Shah was overthrown in 1979 orders for Shir 1 and 2 collapsed, fortunately before any deliveries could be made. The British Government was now faced with an acute problem: the loss of the Shir orders meant a significant loss of work for the Royal Ordnance Factory at Leeds, spelling heavy redundancies with obvious political consequences. It was decided therefore to exploit the development already carried out for, and incidentally largely paid by, the Shah of Iran. The Shir 2 was modified slightly to enable it to operate in the harsher Western European environment, was rechristened Challenger, and was put into immediate production for the British Army. Thus the jobs of the highly skilled workers in Leeds were saved and the British Army received a superb tank a full decade earlier than had been expected.

Good power-to-weight

Challenger is powered by a Rolls-Royce Condor 12V-1200 diesel engine, fitted with Garret-AiResearch turbochargers. Despite its high combat weight of 60 tonnes, Challenger has a respectable power-to-weight ratio of 21.74 hp/tonne compared with 15.61 hp/tonne of the Chieftain, and can develop a sustained maximum road speed of 56 km/h (35 mph).

Challenger is armed with the old 120-mm L11A5 rifled gun, which may be replaced eventually by a new high-pressure gun capable of firing the same varied range of ammunition.

Varied weapons

Up to 52 rounds of assorted High Explosive Squash Head (HESH), Armour Piercing Discarding Sabot (APDS), Armour Piercing Fin-Stabilized Discarding Sabot (APFSDS) Smoke and Practice can be carried.

A HESH round, having struck its target, compresses onto the outer skin. Shock waves caused by the resulting

Inside the Challenger

Challenger is one of the most capable Main Battle Tanks in the world, and its introduction to the Royal Armoured Corps substantially improves the fighting power of the British Army of the Rhine. Unfortunately, Britain's defence budget is not being stretched to allow Challenger to completely replace Chieftain.

Powerpack
The whole powerpack weighs nearly 5.5 tonnes, but is designed for quick replacement in the field. The existing Army armoured repair vehicle, FV 434, cannot cope with the weight so a new vehicle based on the Chieftain chassis has had to be introduced.

Rolls-Royce Condor 12V 1200 engine
Based on proven conventional components, this is an excellent engine with low specific fuel consumption. It uses high efficiency turbo chargers and can develop 1200 bhp at 2300 revolutions per minute. The same engine is fitted to the Khalid tank, essentially a Chieftain with a Challenger powerpack sold to Jordan.

120-mm L11A5 rifled gun
Challenger's main armament is fitted with a thermal sleeve, fume extractor and muzzle reference system. The L30 high-pressure tank gun will be retro-fitted to the Challenger force when it enters service.

Gunner
BAOR Challengers are fitted with TOGS (Thermal Observation and Gunnery System) which lives in an armoured barbette on the right of the turret and provides separate outputs for commander and gunner.

Single pin track
Challenger's track is not interchangeable with Chieftain's. It is a single-pin track with removable rubber pads, although this may be replaced with a new track which offers less rolling resistance and has a longer life expectancy.

Chobham armour
Still highly classified, Chobham armour is named after the MoD establishment where it was first developed. It is particularly effective against chemical energy attack, so infantry anti-tank rockets and anti-tank guided missiles present much less of a threat to Challenger than they do to Chieftain.

explosion cause the inner surface of the target to fracture, flake off and fly around until contact is made with a crew member or, more drastically, stored ammunition.

The more advanced APDS and APFSDS rounds consist of a sub-calibre projectile with a Sabot, or lightly sectioned 'sleeve', fitting the residue of the bore. Once the round is fired the Sabot splits and falls away, leaving the projectile to travel at very high speed until it strikes and forces its way through the target.

Gun fit

An L7A2 7.62-mm machine-gun is fitted co-axially with the main armament and another 7.62-mm GPMG is mounted on the commander's cupola,

With a combat weight of over 60 tonnes, Challenger needs a formidable powerpack to give it enough mobility to survive on the modern battlefield.

Gunnery equipment
The gunner has a tank laser sight with a magnification of ×1 and ×10. The laser rangefinder can be used up to 10,000 metres and is usually accurate to within 10 metres. The fire control system uses a more modern computer than that installed in Chieftain and it has great capacity for 'stretch'.

Commander's machine-gun
The commander's cupola has a 7.62-mm L37A2 machine-gun for rather optimistic anti-aircraft defence. The co-axial 7.62 mm L8A2 machine-gun is of much greater value since it can be fired from within the vehicle.

Commander
He has a modified No. 15 cupola which is fitted either with a day sight or image intensifier for night combat. Nine periscopes provide the commander with all-round vision.

Loader
His task is to load the Challenger's 64 rounds of 120-mm ammunition: generally 20 'fin' and 44 HESH and smoke rounds. The ammunition is separate. Each charge storage position contains either one charge for an APDSFS round or two for HESH/smoke.

Driver
The driver can swing his single-piece hatch forward so he can drive with his head out. He has a wide angle periscope for day driving, which can be replaced by a Pilkington passive night sight for driving in conditions of darkness. In an emergency the driver can escape through the fighting compartment.

aimed and fired from within the turret. Recent reports suggest that this may be replaced by an old pre-war design Vickers 12.7-mm machine-gun. On the face of it the idea of fitting a tank of the 1990s with a gun of the 1930s may seem ridiculous, but this larger weapon would be far more effective against Soviet helicopters.

Chobham armour

Chobham Armour is as secret as it is revolutionary. Even now, some five years after Challenger made its first appearance with NATO on Exercise Lionheart, little if any open source material exists on the subject.

Conventional spaced or laminated armour can defeat the HESH round, but it is of limited defence against the newer high-velocity APDS rounds,

and it is to defeat these that Chobham Armour was developed.

Many layers

The structure is known to consist of numerous layers of metals, ceramics and plastics designed to absorb and break up the impact of the high-speed core of the APDS round. First sight of Challenger will show not only how immensely thick are the slabs of armour, especially on the forward chassis and turret, but also how angled they are. Indeed, it is suggested

The smooth, uncluttered lines of Challenger are dictated by its Choham armour. The same slab-like construction is evident in the M1 Abrams and Leopard 2: it will be interesting to see if the next Soviet MBT has a similar appearance.

that the 60 per cent angle of the turret armour, not found on earlier British tanks, more than doubles crew protection against all conventional anti-tank

The new British Army combat team: MCV-80 Warrior and Challenger. With the infantry acquiring a much faster APC, the Royal Armoured Corps desperately needed a more mobile MBT than Chieftain.

weapons fired other than at extremely close range.

The exact thickness of the armour can only be assumed, but it is interesting to note that Challenger is some five tonnes heavier than Chieftain Mk V. Although a part of this weight difference is the result of the larger engine, Chobham Armour is as heavy as it is chunky.

Easy maintenance

Thermal imaging sights and a comprehensive NBC system are fitted as standard, and a bolt-on hydro-pneumatic suspension system greatly facilitates maintenance and even replacement in the field. One of the most

Battlefield Evaluation: comparing

Challenger

But for the Ayatollah Khomeini, the failure of the Anglo-German tank programme in 1977 would have left British tank forces solely dependent on their ageing Chieftains. Challenger is a development of the Shah's Shir tank and ranks with the M1 Abrams and Leopard 2 as a Main Battle Tank. Unfortunately, Challenger is not planned to completely replace Chieftain.

Specification:
Combat weight: 62 tonnes
Road speed: 56 km/h
Power-to-weight ratio: 19 hp/tonne
Length: 8.3 m
Height: 2.9 m
Crew: 4
Armament: 1×120-mm gun; 2×7.62-mm machine-guns

Assessment
Firepower   ★★★★★
Protection   ★★★★★
Age   ★
Worldwide users   ★

Once the improvement programme is completed Challenger will rate with the best MBTs currently in service.

T-80

The T-80 has a very low silhouette, even by Soviet standards: the top of its turret barely rises above the hull of an American M60. Allegedly armed with the 'Kobra' gun/missile system, the T-80 is believed to carry advanced armour with panels of reactive armour on top. This provides a high measure of protection against NATO infantry anti-tank weapons.

Specification:
Combat weight: 40 tonnes (estimate)
Road speed: probably over 60 km/h
Power-to-weight ratio: probably over 20 hp/tonne
Length: 6.9 m
Height: 2.2 m
Crew: 3
Armament: 1×125-mm gun/missile launcher; 1×12.7-mm machine-gun; 1×7.62-mm machine-gun

Assessment
Firepower   ★★★★★
Protection   ★★★★
Age   ★
Worldwide users   ★

The T-80 takes Soviet insistence on a low silhouette to its logical extreme and presents a very small target.

M1 Abrams

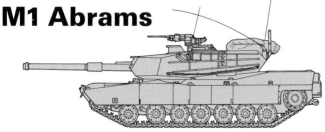

Heavily armoured but incredibly agile, the M1 is proving highly successful with US armoured units in West Germany. Soviet reactive armour makes their tanks almost invulnerable to weapons like LAW and Carl Gustav, so NATO's defences will rely more than ever on the tank forces; the M1s, Leopard 2s and Challengers are excellent vehicles but whether there are enough of them is open to question.

Specification:
Combat weight: 54.5 tonnes
Road speed: 72 km/h
Power-to-weight ratio: 27 hp/tonne
Length: 7.9 m
Height: 2.8 m
Crew: 4
Armament: 1×120-mm Rheinmetall smoothbore gun; 2×7.62-mm machine-guns, 1×12.7-mm machine-gun

Assessment
Firepower   ★★★★★
Protection   ★★★★★
Age   ★★
Worldwide users   ★

Instead of the familiar deep rumble of a diesel, M1 Abrams tanks produce a distinctive high-pitched whine.

versatile of tanks in service anywhere, Challenger can climb gradients of 60 per cent, overcome vertical obstacles as high as 0.9 m and cross trenches up to three metres wide.

It is the intention of the British Army to buy some 400 Challengers, enough to equip seven of its armoured regiments. According to figures published by the International Institute of Strategic Studies in autumn 1986 there were 250 Challengers then in service. Production at the Leeds factory, sold by Royal Ordnance to Vickers in October 1986, continues at present, although it is not known whether or not manufacture will stop when the current order is completed.

Challenger is well armed, well armoured and equipped with an excellent fire control system. Unfortunately Challenger is not planned to completely replace Chieftain, and it is not known whether production will continue.

the Challenger with its rivals

Leopard 2

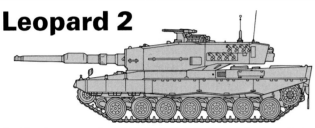

The West German army has a Main Battle Tank that is equal, if not superior, to the M1 Abrams and has a very well trained tank crew. The Leopard 2 is exceptionally mobile with tremendous acceleration, and it can shoot accurately while moving. Unlike Challenger, it has blow-off panels above the ammunition storage area in the turret rear, which are supposed to prevent a catastrophic secondary explosion if that part of the turret is penetrated.

Specification:
Combat weight: 55 tonnes
Road speed: 72 km/h
Power-to-weight ratio: 27 hp/tonne
Length: 7.72 m
Height: 2.48 m
Crew: 4
Armament: 1×120-mm Rheinmetall smoothbore gun; 2×7.62-mm machine-guns

Assessment
Firepower	★★★★★
Protection	★★★★★
Age	★★★
Worldwide users	★★

Leopard 2 was developed after the failure of an Anglo-German tank development programme.

T-72

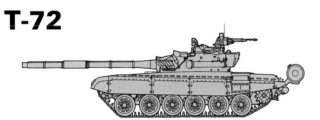

The T-72 will probably be the most numerous tank in Warsaw Pact service for the next 10 or 20 years. Its armour cannot keep out NATO 105-mm APDSFS, but reactive armour panels protect it against infantry anti-tank weapons. The T-72 is a less capable tank than Challenger but not hopelessly inferior, and every year since 1978 the Soviets have built more T-72s than the entire production run of Challenger.

Specification:
Combat weight: 41 tonnes
Road speed: 60 km/h
Power-to-weight ratio: 19 hp/tonne
Length: 6.95 m
Height: 2.37 m
Crew: 3
Armament: 1×125-mm gun; 1×12.7-mm machine-gun; 1×7.62-mm machine-gun

Assessment
Firepower	★★★★★
Protection	★★★
Age	★★★
Worldwide users	★★★

A column of Soviet Army T-72s: Challenger's main opponent in a future conflict in Europe.

Chieftain

Chieftain was the best MBT of its generation, but it was always underpowered and ageing powerplants continue to produce mechanical problems. Royal Ordnance produced some interesting ideas to follow Chieftain but they were not funded. Challenger is a development of the Chieftain design, but is far more agile and its armament is aimed at using up-to-date computer fire control systems.

Specification:
Combat weight: 54 tonnes
Road speed: 56 km/h
Power-to-weight ratio: 19 hp/tonne
Length: 8.3 m
Height: 2.9 m
Crew: 4
Armament: 1×120-mm gun; 2×7.62-mm machine-guns

Assessment
Firepower	★★★★★
Protection	★★★★★
Age	★
Worldwide users	★

Chieftains will remain the most numerous tank in British service for many years to come.

Zap it with a Steyr

The Steyr AUG is an excellent combat rifle despite its unorthodox appearance. The optical sight provides X1.5 magnification and has a black ring as its reticle. Place this over a man-sized target at up to 300 metres and you should nail him every time.

The Steyr AUG looks quite unlike any other modern rifle, and seems more like a prop from a Star Wars movie than a serious military weapon. However, despite its unconventional appearance, the Steyr is an excellent gun and is proving increasingly successful in the cut-throat world of international firearms.

The AUG was developed by the Steyr-Daimler-Puch company for the Austrian army, which wanted to replace its ageing FN FALs. The Steyr factory still manufactures the splendid Männlicher sporting rifles, but to meet the military requirements they produced a revolutionary weapon.

Bullpup rifle

First, Steyr decided to make a bull-pup rifle. A bullpup is a rifle which has the action set back in the stock so that the breech is alongside the firer's face and the magazine, therefore, is behind the trigger. Bullpups were not exactly new, but they had only ever been proposed for a military rifle once before – the British EM1 of 1950 – which failed to reach service.

Second, they decided to utilise modern plastic material instead of wood. Third, the rifle was to be modular, so that the component parts could be shuffled around to produce a number of different weapons – hence the name 'AUG', for Army Universal Gun. And it had to be in 5.56-mm calibre, since that appeared to be the coming thing.

The Austrian army played a considerable part in the initial concept

THE AUGUST SYSTEM

The carbine version of the AUG is 69 cm long. Barrel length is reduced to 407 mm, 101 mm less than the rifle.

The HBAR (Heavy Barrel Automatic Rifle) is the LMG version of the AUG and is fitted with a 42-round magazine.

The AUG rifle (above) and the paratrooper's carbine version, which is 62.6 cm long and has a fixed barrel grip instead of the flexible one on the rifle.

Above: Austrian troops wade through a marsh, keeping their AUGs clear of the mud. Note how the man on the right has folded down the foregrip.

Left: The sights on the AUG are easy to learn how to use and provide a high degree of accuracy. Like the SUSAT sight on the SA80, the Steyr's sight is a great improvement over iron sights when shooting in bad light conditions.

The Steyr AUG has proved itself to be a very sturdy piece of kit despite fears that a largely plastic gun would not be strong enough for service use.

The AUG rifle with an optical night sight above it, mounted on the alternative receiver group.

definition phase, and among other things they insisted on a twist of rifling of one turn in 9 inches. This was very forward-looking; at that time the only 5.56-mm service cartridge was the American M193 which used a 7-inch twist. But the army knew that there were better bullets in the pipeline, bullets which would demand a slower twist, so they specified 9 inches which, as it turned out, was an ideal compromise between the then-standard and the newer NATO standard of 12 inches, which appeared some years later. The AUG will shoot either type of 5.56-mm ammunition equally accurately.

Component parts

The plastic stock has the trigger, sear rod, safety and locking catches incorporated; everything else is then added in removable form. The receiver is fitted with lugs to accept the barrel in the front end and the bolt in the rear, and it has the gas cylinder formed on the right side and a spring cylinder on the left.

The bolt carrier is attached to two rods, which slide into these cylinders and have the return springs permanently attached. The bolt locks into the carrier by a pin which, riding in a curved slot in the carrier, gives the bolt a rotary motion to lock and unlock. The receiver and bolt unit then slip into the plastic stock and are retained by a simple catch.

Carrying handle

The barrel then slides in and locks into the receiver lugs. An all-plastic hammer unit slips into the rear of the stock and is retained in place by the butt plate. The receiver is shaped into a carrying handle, which also holds a 1.4x optical sight. The magazine is a transparent plastic unit holding 30 rounds in a double column.

There is a folding handle fitted to the barrel, which helps when removing it and also acts as a front grip; you can grip it upright or fold it forward for a more 'rifle-like' grip. The aiming mark on the telescope is simply a circle. Place the circle around the target, press the trigger, and you invariably hit what you aimed at. Give the

Inside the Steyr AUG

The revolutionary Steyr is rapidly becoming the most popular bullpup assault rifle in the world. Now sold to Australia and New Zealand and Oman, it is under consideration by several other armies. The simplicity of the sights makes it easier to teach recruits to shoot with, and the interchangeable parts allow an army to buy a whole weapons system built around common elements.

Cocking handle
With forward-assist locking button on its rear end, which when pressed locks the handle to the bolt mechanism and allows you to slam the bolt closed on a sticky cartridge.

Barrel

Flash eliminator

22-mm bearings
These allow the AUG to fire any NATO standard rifle grenade.

Bayonet lug
This is not fitted to all models of the AUG.

Gas regulator
This can be adjusted to admit more gas to the piston to overcome dirt in the weapon or a dry mechanism. It can also be entirely shut off for grenade firing.

Barrel release
Press this down and back to unlock the barrel for removal.

Trigger operating rod
This carries the trigger movement back to the firing mechanism.

Front grip
This is either in this position or folded forward to lie underneath the barrel. It also acts as a handle when you are changing the barrel.

Trigger
Pull lightly for single shots and pull it all the way back to get automatic fire.

Left: The Steyr AUG is designed to be a light and handy assault rifle. Unlike the SA80 it can be modified for left-handed operation, and by swapping the component parts you can make an LMG or SMG instead.

trigger a harder squeeze and the rifle then fires full-automatic at 650 rounds a minute; there is no change lever to adjust.

The Steyr field-stripped:
1 Barrel assembly
2 Housing assembly
3 Bolt assembly
4 Stock
5 Hammer group
6 Magazine
7 Butt plate

NOTE: The Steyr's take-down catch is on the right-hand side by the ejection port.

The circle in the sight is designed to cover a 1.8 metre diameter at 300 metres range, which means that it can be a useful aid to rangefinding; if the circle almost fits around the average man, he must be about 300 metres away. But, in fact, rangefinding is scarcely vital with this weapon; the trajectory is so flat that you can take the same point of aim at any range to 350 metres and hit the target. And because there is only one aiming device, the recruit no longer has to worry about getting two sights and the target in perfect alignment, so that teaching men to shoot with this rifle is very easy.

Trial of strength

All very well, you say, but who wants a rifle with plastic furniture and a cast aluminium receiver in combat? At a demonstration at Steyr some years ago an AUG was thrown on to stony ground and run over repeatedly by a variety of vehicles; after surviving 10 passes by a Land Rover, 10 by a one-ton and 10 by a three-ton, it survived three from a six-tonner before the receiver sight bracket cracked. The rifle was still perfectly serviceable, and the plastic was not only unbroken but also unscarred.

In another test a loose bullet was driven into the bore by a hammer and punch, after which the rifle was assembled, loaded, and fired – from a man's shoulder. Nothing untoward happened, except that it kicked slightly more than usual and the cap of the cartridge blew out into the plastic stock. But the barrel was perfectly

Zap it with a Steyr

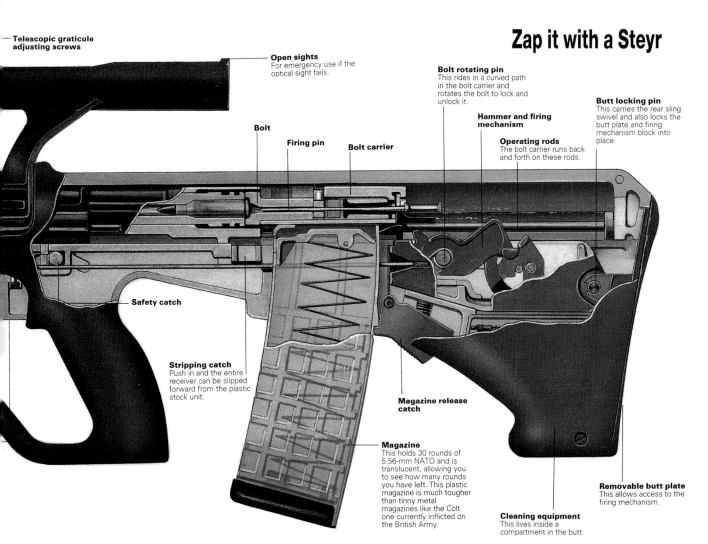

Telescopic graticule adjusting screws

Open sights
For emergency use if the optical sight fails.

Bolt

Firing pin

Bolt carrier

Bolt rotating pin
This rides in a curved path in the bolt carrier and rotates the bolt to lock and unlock it.

Hammer and firing mechanism

Operating rods
The bolt carrier runs back and forth on these rods.

Butt locking pin
This carries the rear sling swivel and also locks the butt plate and firing mechanism block into place.

Safety catch

Stripping catch
Push in and the entire receiver can be slipped forward from the plastic stock unit.

Magazine release catch

Magazine
This holds 30 rounds of 5.56-mm NATO and is translucent, allowing you to see how many rounds you have left. This plastic magazine is much tougher than tinny metal magazines like the Colt one currently inflicted on the British Army.

Cleaning equipment
This lives inside a compartment in the butt.

Removable butt plate
This allows access to the firing mechanism.

undamaged. Also, a barrel has been filled with water over a loaded round and fired without damage. Try that on your . . . well, perhaps better not. Very few rifles will survive that sort of treatment.

As to the 'Universal' part of the name; firstly, you can swap four barrel lengths – 621 mm for the light machine-gun version, 508 mm for the rifle, 407 mm for the carbine and 350 mm for the sub-machine gun version.

Versatility

You can fit a bipod and 42-round magazine if you are using it as a light machine-gun. You can remove the receiver with optical sight and replace it with one having a NATO-standard mounting bracket, which will accept any kind of optical sight or night vision sight.

You can take out the hammer unit and replace it with one which gives semi-automatic fire only; or with one which gives single shots or three-round bursts; or with one which allows you to select full automatic or three-round bursts by moving a switch on the unit before you fit it into the rifle.

Steyr makes the plastic stock in

The Steyr can take a scope mount in place of the integral optical sight. This allows it to carry almost any scope you like. Quick-change mounts allow you to swap sights rapidly without having to resight the weapon.

A Steyr AUG with some magazines, 5.56-mm ammunition and a pair of rifle grenades. By keeping the design as simple and basic as possible, Steyr have produced a 'soldier proof' weapon which is also highly accurate in capable hands. The police version has a dot in the centre of the sight picture for better accuracy.

olive green, sand colour or black; but if you fancy a pink stock or a purple one, it'll oblige – so long as you buy enough of them.

The last adaptation appeared in 1985; the '9-mm AUG Para'. This is something of a major refit, but it still uses the basic components. The 5.56-mm short barrel is changed for a 9-mm barrel, the locking bolt and carrier unit are exchanged for a blowback bolt, and an adapter in the magazine well accepts a new magazine carrying 32 9-mm cartridges. The result is a very effective and accurate sub-machine-gun.

The Austrian army adopted the AUG as the 'Sturmgewehr '77'. After

Battlefield Evaluation: comparing

Steyr AUG

Specification:
Cartridge: 5.56mm×45
Weight: 4.1kg
Length: 79cms overall
Cyclic rate of fire: 65 rounds per minute
Magazine: 30 rounds

The Steyr AUG has few rivals as a weapons system. Like the SA80 and LSW, the AUG provides a rifle and light machine-gun which use the same mechanism, but the Austrian system is far more comprehensive. The carbine and paratrooper weapons are excellent close-quarter weapons, and the 9-mm version is a shrewdly designed gun which may make considerable impact in the sub-machine gun market.

Assessment
Reliability	★★★★
Accuracy	★★★★
Age	★★
Worldwide users	★★

By swapping various assemblies the Steyr can be altered to different configurations. This is the LMG.

FA MAS

Specification:
Cartridge: 5.56mm
Weight: 4.5kg
Length: 75.7cms
Cyclic rate of fire: 1000 rounds per minute
Magazine: 25-round box

The French FA MAS bullpup assault rifle makes extensive use of reinforced plastic and high-strength glass fibre. Like the Steyr it has an advantage over the SA80 in that you can quickly alter the weapon to shoot left-handed. It is capable of single-shot, three-round bursts or fully automatic fire, and in the case of the latter the extremely high rate of fire makes short bursts highly accurate. A bipod is fitted as standard for better shooting from the prone position.

Assessment
Reliability	★★★★
Accuracy	★★★★
Age	★★
Worldwide users	★★

The FA MAS is a well-designed bullpup assault rifle capable of right- and left-handed operation.

SA80

Specification:
Cartridge: 5.56mm
Weight: 5kg
Length: 78.5cms
Cyclic rate of fire: 800 rounds per minute
Magazine: 30-round box

The SA80 is performing well in British service, although a few minor problems have surfaced as more regiments have been issued with them. The magazine catch needs strengthening and the way insect repellent melts the plastic stock should be attended to. However, SA80 is a great improvement over the SLR and a far more sensible weapon for mechanised infantry.

Assessment
Reliability	★★★★
Accuracy	★★★★
Age	★★
Worldwide users	★★

The SA80 is a sound weapon but lags inexcusably far behind the AUG in the export market.

that it was taken up in some numbers by the Moroccan, Omani and Saudi armies, and in 1985 was officially adopted as the next rifle for the Australian and New Zealand armies. It is also under consideration by other armies, among them the Irish, and it will undoubtedly be taken into service elsewhere before 1990. It may look like a toy, but in many opinions the AUG is the best 5.56-mm rifle in the world today.

A Steyr AUG light machine-gun undergoes its mud test. To dispel any doubts about the strength of the plastic AUG, Steyr conducted a series of brutal experiments which it proved to be one of the toughest firearms ever made.

the Steyr AUG with its rivals

M16A2

The M16A2 is essentially the M16 modified to fire the new NATO standard 5.56-mm round and incorporates a number of improvements over the M16A1. Colt will supply the weapon capable of fully automatic fire, but the US Army has elected to buy rifles only capable of three-round bursts. Still as light and handy as the original, the M16A2 is a first-class assault rifle.

Specification:
Cartridge: 5.56 mm×45
Weight: 3.85 kg
Length: 100 cms
Cyclic rate of fire: 600 rounds per minute
Magazine: 30-round box

Assessment
Reliability   ★★★★
Accuracy   ★★★★
Age   ★
Worldwide users ★★★

The M16A2 is a more conventional rifle than the AUG but was beaten in the competition for the Australian army.

AK-74

Easily distinguishable from the AKM by the groove in the butt and the different muzzle brake, the AK-74 fires the controversial 5.45-mm×39 cartridge. The muzzle brake helps keep the recoil very low although it reportedly produces a telltale muzzle flash. Airborne and other specialist units use the AKS-74, which has a tubular folding butt that swings to the left to lie against the receiver.

Specification:
Cartridge: 5.45 mm×39
Weight: 3.6 kg unloaded
Length: 93 cms
Cyclic rate of fire: 650 rounds per minute
Magazine: 30-round plastic box

Assessment
Reliability   ★★★★
Accuracy   ★★★
Age   ★★
Worldwide users ★★★

The AK-47 follows the evolutionary pattern of the Kalashnikov but is inferior to the AUG.

Galil

The Galil is an excellent assault rifle in either 7.62-mm or 5.56-mm calibre. A very sturdy piece of kit, the design may not be terribly original; but the Galil shoots very well and is very tolerant of dirt and debris. Galils had tritium night sights fitted as standard for shooting in poor light conditions.

Specification:
Cartridge: 5.56 mm×45
Weight: 5.2 kg
Length: 97.9 mm
Cyclic rate of fire: 650 rounds per minute
Magazine: 35- or 50-round box

Assessment
Reliability   ★★★★
Accuracy   ★★★★
Age   ★★★
Worldwide users ★★★

The Galil is a combat rifle of proven strength and efficiency.

Tank-Killing Cobra

Squatting in a foxhole, you can hear the rumble of approaching armour above the noise of battle and a distant chop-chop of rotor blades. A bright light flashes across the sky above your retreat, followed by a distant thud. The rumble ceases, and a Cobra appears from the trees behind you, gun turret traversing the treeline beyond you for signs of movement.

As the helicopter manoeuvres into open ground, two small flashes of gunfire spring from the treeline. The gun turret spews a two-second burst into the vegetation, raking a 20-yard section. There are no more muzzle flashes. As you marvel at the clinical killing power of this fearsome brute, it is gone, lifting its tail so that the rotor blades nearly hit the ground in front of it, accelerating from a walking pace to over 100 knots in a few seconds.

Cobra mission

Such is the game of the Bell Model 209, designated the AH-1 by the US Army but universally known as the Cobra. Its job now is to provide fire support and attack enemy armour, but 20 years ago when it entered service it hunted Vietnamese communists in the jungles and forests of South-East Asia.

Early successes in the Vietnam war with heavily-armed Bell UH-1 Hueys led Bell to develop a specialist gunship version which employed many of the components of the Huey, attached to a new, sleek fuselage. Pilot and gunner were seated in the now classic gunship configuration, with the gunner in the front commanding an uninterrupted view ahead of the machine. With tandem seating, the designers achieved a very small frontal cross section, making the helicopter an extremely small target from head-on. Weapons were to be carried under two stub wings attached to the side of the fuselage, and in a chin turret.

Development ran quickly, and in 1967 the first examples of the AH-1G reached Vietnam, after the type's first flight in September 1965. Deliveries were swift to the theatre, and the AH-1 soon proved itself as one of the most important weapons operating in South-East Asia. Combat operations often included fire support of ground forces, whereby ground commanders could call up the gunships when they faced superior forces. Helicopter escort was another major role, the Cobras riding 'shotgun' to the troop-carrying Hueys until a few miles short of their LZ, when they would speed ahead and soften up the LZ, making it safe for the 'slicks' to land.

Weapon fits were many, with the chin turret able to take either two 7.62-mm machine-guns or 40-mm grenade-launchers, or one of each. Further gun pods could be carried

Left: Modern anti-armour helicopter operations require the aircraft to fly as low as possible, using any cover available. Trees are a favourite hide.

Right: The Marines fly the Cobra from assault carriers in support of troops in contact. All Marine models have two engines for overwater safety.

Below: The shape of the AH-1 is much changed from its Vietnam days, with flat-pane canopy, new gun turret, TOW launchers and infra-red countermeasures.

under the stub wings, in addition to rocket pods. While most served with the Army, others went to the Marine Corps, which eventually received its twin-engined AH-1J version in 1970, this variant being considered safer for over-water operations.

Tank-killer

With the Vietnam war over, Bell developed the Cobra for the anti-armour role, although the aircraft was still able to perform its previous roles. The main modification lay in the adoption of the TOW anti-tank missile, of which eight could be carried under the stub wings. So equipped, the first TOW Cobras were designated AH-1Q, followed by the AH-1R which featured an uprated engine but no TOW capability. Finally the AH-1S brought both modifications together.

Even so, AH-1S aircraft have existed in many different configurations, and the shape of the Cobra has evolved to incorporate a new chin turret with a three-barrel 20-mm cannon, an angular flat-pane canopy, infra-red countermeasures turret and various infra-red suppressors on the exhaust. The first of these was an upturned unit, but now a special suppressor has been added to the exhaust.

During the mid-1980s, the fully modernised AH-1S aircraft were designated AH-1F, and the US Army hopes to modernise all its fleet to this

Right: This view shows to good effect the small frontal cross-section presented by the Cobra, making it a difficult target to hit in a head-to-head situation.

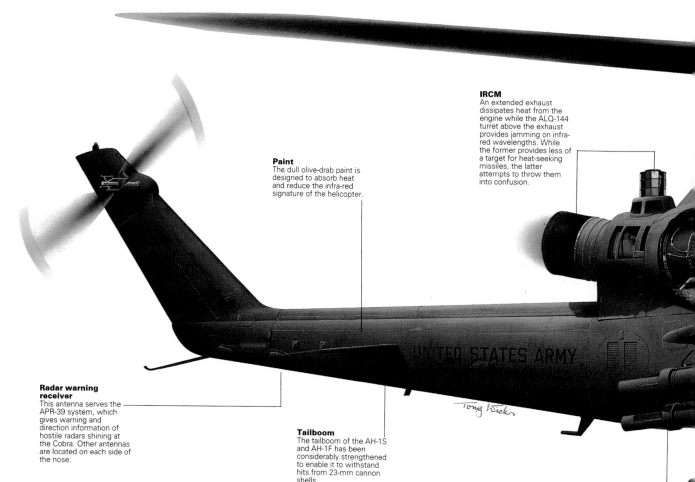

IRCM
An extended exhaust dissipates heat from the engine while the ALQ-144 turret above the exhaust provides jamming on infra-red wavelengths. While the former provides less of a target for heat-seeking missiles, the latter attempts to throw them into confusion.

Paint
The dull olive-drab paint is designed to absorb heat and reduce the infra-red signature of the helicopter.

Radar warning receiver
This antenna serves the APR-39 system, which gives warning and direction information of hostile radars shining at the Cobra. Other antennas are located on each side of the nose.

Tailboom
The tailboom of the AH-1S and AH-1F has been considerably strengthened to enable it to withstand hits from 23-mm cannon shells.

TOW tubes
TOW tubes and their missiles come in modules of two, four modules being the usual load for the AH-1. After launch, fins pop out to stabilise the missile in flight.

standard, although many AH-1S helicopters exist in lesser stages of conversion. The Marine Corps too has introduced better models, the first being the AH-1T with uprated engine and dynamic system, which soon gained TOW capability. In the late 1980s they are receiving AH-1W aircraft with even greater power and new weapons options such as the Sidewinder air-to-air missile. Marine Corps aircraft have seen action in the Gulf.

Other nations operate the Cobra on similar tasks to the US Army, including Iran, Israel, Japan, Jordan, Pakistan and South Korea. Those of Israel have seen extensive action against Syria, while the AH-1Js of Iran have been used in the Gulf war with Iraq. Numbers serving with these nations is small compared with the 1,200 in service with the US Army, and 170 with the USMC, the latter having put its aircraft to use during the invasion of Grenada.

Laser augmentation

So how does the Cobra operate in the anti-armour role? For delivery of its principal weapon, the TOW missile, it utilises a Laser Augmented Airborne TOW sight mounted in the extreme nose. This sight allows the gunner to spot targets at long range, and then guide the TOW missile by thermal imaging on to the target. Laser

The Cobra is air-transportable with a minimum of fuss, easily accommodated by the Lockheed C-5 Galaxy, allowing rapid deployment to any spot on the globe.

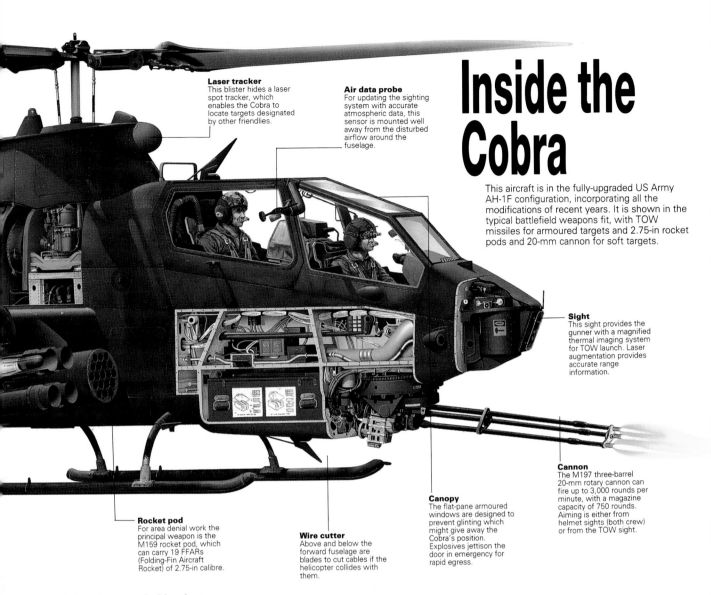

Laser tracker
This blister hides a laser spot tracker, which enables the Cobra to locate targets designated by other friendlies.

Air data probe
For updating the sighting system with accurate atmospheric data, this sensor is mounted well away from the disturbed airflow around the fuselage.

Inside the Cobra

This aircraft is in the fully-upgraded US Army AH-1F configuration, incorporating all the modifications of recent years. It is shown in the typical battlefield weapons fit, with TOW missiles for armoured targets and 2.75-in rocket pods and 20-mm cannon for soft targets.

Sight
This sight provides the gunner with a magnified thermal imaging system for TOW launch. Laser augmentation provides accurate range information.

Cannon
The M197 three-barrel 20-mm rotary cannon can fire up to 3,000 rounds per minute, with a magazine capacity of 750 rounds. Aiming is either from helmet sights (both crew) or from the TOW sight.

Canopy
The flat-pane armoured windows are designed to prevent glinting which might give away the Cobra's position. Explosives jettison the door in emergency for rapid egress.

Wire cutter
Above and below the forward fuselage are blades to cut cables if the helicopter collides with them.

Rocket pod
For area denial work the principal weapon is the M159 rocket pod, which can carry 19 FFARs (Folding-Fin Aircraft Rocket) of 2.75-in calibre.

augmentation is provided by designators situated either on the ground or more likely in an airborne scout helicopter such as the Bell OH-58D, which 'spots' the target with a laser. This shows in the gunner's sight, allowing him to guide the missile from far greater ranges than if he were using purely optical sighting.

With the four-round TOW launcher occupying the outer pylon on each wing, the inner pylon can be used primarily for 2.75-in rocket pods, available in 7- or 19-tube versions. These weapons are aimed in a shallow dive, as usually is the chin gun. Both rockets and gun are used for fire support of friendly troops, and due to the normal attack profile are used in areas away from intense groundfire.

Helicopters are vulnerable wherever they can be clearly seen, so it is better for the Cobra to operate from cover as much as possible. Ingress and egress are made at below treetop height, the aircraft popping-up above just to acquire, aim and guide the TOW missiles. To avoid attack, the

Scout helicopters provide the Cobra with much of its targetting information. In current use with the US Army is the Bell OH-58 Kiowa, shown here with an AH-1F.

AH-1F is fitted with a radar warning receiver and an infra-red counter-measures turret behind the rotor mast. Armour is incorporated into the aircraft around the cockpit. In the future Cobras will be configured to carry air-to-air missiles to defend themselves or to act as fighters over the battlefield, taking on both enemy aircraft and helicopters.

Marine Corps AH-1s are already configured for air-to-air missiles, but their main job remains close support of Marine assaults. Based on assault carriers alongside Boeing Vertol CH-46 Sea Knight troopers, the AH-1s would escort helicopters and landing craft during the initial assault, and

The Sidewinder air-to-air missile is operational on Marine AH-1s, like this example on Guadalcanal in the Persian Gulf. Note the flare dispenser above the stub wing.

Battlefield Evaluation: comparing

Bell AH-1F HueyCobra

Standard Cobra model for the US Army is the single-engined AH-1F, available in large numbers. Particular attention has been paid to low detectability, with the carriage of an infra-red suppressed exhaust and an IR jammer in addition to radar warning receiver. It has been exported to several nations.

Specification:
Length overall: 16.18m
Rotor diameter: 13.41m
Maximum cruising speed: 123 knots
Range: 507km
Standard weapon load: eight TOW anti-tank missiles; one three-barrelled 20-mm cannon; two unguided rocket or cannon pods

Assessment
Manoeuvrability ***
All weather capability *
Versatility *
Worldwide users ****

Cobras are available to the US Army in huge numbers, and are still a highly potent anti-armour platform.

Bell AH-1T and AH-1W

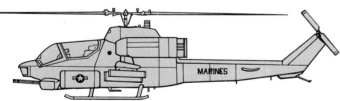

The AH-1T is the current US Marine Corps version, soon to be superseded by the AH-1W SuperCobra with uprated engines. Differing primarily from the Army Cobras by having twin engines for overwater safety, the Marine Corps aircraft carry different ordnance loads, including the Hellfire missile in the case of the AH-1W.

Specification:
Length overall: 17.68m
Rotor diameter: 14.63m
Maximum cruising speed: 189 knots
Range: 635km
Standard weapon load: eight TOW or Hellfire anti-tank missiles; one three-barrel 20-mm cannon; up to 76 2.75-in unguided rockets or 16 5-in Zuni rockets or cannon pods or two AIM-9Ls Sidewinder air-to-

Assessment
Manoeuvrability ***
All weather capability ***
Versatility ***
Worldwide users **

Marine AH-1Ts have seen action during the invasion of Grenada. This aircraft is taking off from Guam.

McDonnell Douglas AH-64 Apache

By comparison with the Cobra, the Apache possesses far greater capability in the form of sophisticated avionics and weapons (Hellfire missiles), yet it is more cumbersome and more difficult to maintain in the field. The disadvantage of having no roof- or mast-mounted sight is shared with the HueyCobra.

Specification:
Length overall: 17.76m
Rotor diameter: 14.63m
Maximum cruising speed: 155 knots
Range: 482km
Standard weapon load: M230 30-mm Chain Gun; 16 Hellfire anti-tank missiles or eight Hellfires and two rocket pods

Assessment
Manoeuvrability ***
All weather capability *****
Versatility **
Worldwide users *

Far more sophisticated than the AH-1, the AH-64 has all-weather attack capability and laser-guided missiles.

then support the Marines once ashore at the beachhead.

Although nowhere near so sophisticated as the McDonnell Douglas AH-64 Apache now in service, the Cobra is still a highly valued asset in the battlefield, and available in such large numbers that its impact on any armoured conflict would be huge. Despite being over 20 years old, the airframe has plenty of room for improvement: certainly the adoption of a roof- or mast-mounted sight would render it less vulnerable in the face of heavy defences. One of the great successes of the Vietnam war, Bell's Cobra is still in business, and will be so for years to come.

A close-up of an AH-1 shows the stepped cockpit, with the gunner in the forward position commanding an all-round view ahead. The pilot sits higher to see over the gunner's position.

the Cobra with its rivals

Westland Lynx AH.Mk 1

Its larger size and lack of gun make the Lynx less dedicated to the anti-armour role, yet its ability to carry troops or reloads in the cabin are of great use on the battlefield. A roof-mounted sight allows it to fire its TOW missiles from a semi-concealed position. The projected Lynx 3 will introduce Hellfire.

Specification:
Length overall: 15.163 m
Rotor diameter: 12.80 m
Maximum cruising speed: 140 knots
Range: 540 km
Standard weapon load: eight TOW missiles

Assessment
Manoeuvrability ★★★★★
All weather capability ★
Versatility ★★★★★
Worldwide users ★

Seen transiting at high level, the Lynx is at its best down in the trees, where it displays astonishing agility.

Agusta A 129 Mangusta

The Mangusta is comparable with the AH-1, being a dedicated attack helicopter with TOW missiles and a low visual signature, while lacking some of the sophisticated avionics of the Apache. Although not yet fitted, the Mangusta has provision for a mast-mounted sight.

Specification:
Length overall: 14.29 m
Rotor diameter: 11.90 m
Maximum cruising speed: 140 knots
Range: not quoted
Standard weapon load: eight TOW missiles; two rocket or 20-mm cannon pods

Assessment
Manoeuvrability ★★★
All weather capability ★★★★
Versatility ★★
Worldwide users ★

*Quad **TOW** tubes and rocket pods on each wing replicate the **Cobra**'s warload, but there is no gun turret.*

Mil Mi-24 'Hind-E'

Large and unmanoeuvrable, the 'Hind' maintains a measure of survivability by being fast and well-armoured. Large numbers of unguided rockets can be carried, with a nose-mounted cannon, but only four guided missiles can be carried. The 'Hind's' forte would seem to lie in joint attack/assault missions.

Specification:
Length overall: 21.50 m
Rotor diameter: 17.00 m
Maximum cruising speed: 159 knots
Range: 750 km
Standard weapon load: four UV-32-57 rocket pods; four AT-6 'Spiral' anti-tank missiles; one four-barrel 12.7-mm cannon

Assessment
Manoeuvrability ★
All weather capability ★
Versatility ★★★
Worldwide users ★★★★★

This Polish air force machine is a 'Hind-D', with AT-2 missile capability. The 'Hind-E' has the better AT-6.

DESERT SURVIVAL

Desert survival was a very real concern to SAS teams deployed to lead local Firqua militia against the Adoo in Oman. Many potential deployment areas such as Eastern Turkey contain deserts, so desert survival is relevant to all units that could be tasked with out-of-area operations.

The very word "desert" conjures up images of shimmering sand dunes and oases of refreshing, sweet, blue water surrounded by vivid green palm trees — but in the Sahara, reality is very different. Only 17 per cent of the Sahara's 3.5 million square miles consists of sand dunes. The rest is a mixture of broken plateaux, weird rock formations, endless gravel, dust plains and arid mountains.

Fear is the enemy

The Sahara, from the Arab word meaning "empty place", is truly vast. Solitude and loneliness, coupled with fear, become a real test of your character and will to survive in this intimidating place.

If you're not acclimatised to the desert, be extremely cautious during

Clothing in the desert must be lightweight and loosely fitting. It must also provide full coverage to protect against sunburn. White cloth will reflect heat, while black will absorb it.

the critical first three or four days of working in summer heat. Sweating washes salts and other minerals out of the body, so make it your business to increase your water and salt intake to compensate.

Avoid salt tablets – they can cause damage to your stomach lining by lying undissolved against the stomach wall. Simple table salt taken with water is adequate. A guide to how much salt you need is taste. If the salt appears to have little or no flavour, increase your intake until it tastes normal again.

Diarrhoea is doubly serious. While you suffer, fluids and essential salts tend to pass unused through the body.

The popular image of the desert as a sea of sand is misleading. There are many different types of desert, all of which provide a very hostile environment. In many areas there is insufficient moisture for animal carcasses to rot.

First Aid kit

An individual first aid kit depends on personal choice and allergies. Seek your doctor's advice if you have any doubt about personal medications. You may also need a prescription for some of the items suggested. Your kit may contain some or all of the following:

Butterfly sutures
Surgical blade
Plasters – assorted sizes and waterproof
Potassium permanganate as general
  disinfectant
Mild pain killers for toothache, headaches e.g.
  Codeine phosphate
Intestinal sedative, e.g. Immodium
Antibiotic cream and tablets
Antihistamine for bites, stings, irritant rashes,
  e.g. Piriton
Water sterilising tablets, e.g. Puritabs
Anti-malaria tablets e.g. Paludrine, Daraprim,
Mepachrin

A comprehensive first-aid kit is essential to deal with the inevitable injuries that accompany any expedition into the desert. Butterfly sutures or Steri-strips are easy to use, and effective for closing wounds that would normally require stitching.

Survival kit

This could be combined with the first aid kit in a single pouch in the pack or on the belt. It is *not* to be treated as a kit to be opened only in an emergency. Use and familiarise yourself with the contents of your kits. Don't wait until you get into trouble before practising your survival techniques.

Wire saw with loop handles
Second compass (button or lapel type)
Fish hooks, line, weights and swivels
Strong needle & thread
Waxed non-safety matches that will strike on
  rough surfaces
Single large candle or three birthday-cake
  candles
Flint and steel
Cotton wool packing for use as fire starting aid
Table salt in small container
Signal flares
Pen torch
Tube of Dextrose tablets
Heliograph
Ground to air recognition tables and morse code
  sheet
Marker panel in fluorescent material
Whistle
Condom for water-carrying

Cooling fluids fail to reach the skin surface in the form of sweat; your body thermostat fails, and you have heat illness as well. Serious sunburn also damages the sweat ducts and so stops the skin surface cooling.

Choose lightweight, loose and comfortable clothes. The looseness provides insulation and prevents excessive evaporation of sweat. Sandals are common favourites for footwear, but beware thorns, snakes and scorpions. If you expect the going to be rocky or difficult, military-pattern or lightweight desert boots are best.

Dehydration

The body absorbs heat from direct sunlight and from the atmosphere. You will also absorb heat reflected from the ground or from direct contact with the ground. Any increase in body

Dawn in the foothills of the Atlas mountains. This apparent wasteland is home for Berber tribesmen who have learnt to survive the rigours of climate and terrain.

Rainfall
It does rain in the desert on high ground and, when it does, rainwater runs off very quickly in the form of flash floods. The floods excavate deep gullies and ravines known as 'wadis'. Vegetation may appear after rain, but the water evaporates very rapidly, leaving the lands as barren as before.

Types of terrain
Each type of terrain seemingly blends into another. There are five different types: mountainous, rocky plateau, sand dune, salt marsh, and highly dissected rocky terrain called 'gebel'.

Survival in a desert, as in any area, depends upon your knowledge of the terrain and the basic climatic elements, your ability to cope with them, and your will to live. Every year the desert continues to kill the unwary, the unprepared and the foolish.

Sand dunes
These are usually extensive areas covered with sand and gravel. Some dunes may be over 300 metres high and 10 to 15 miles long; others will be completely flat. They can be devoid of plant life or covered in scrub up to two metres in height. Any form of travel through sand dune deserts should be avoided.

Salt marshes
This type of terrain has a highly corrosive effect on boots, clothing and skin.

Rocky plateau dese
These are characterise many solid or broken r at or near the surface, there may be sand dur around the plateau. Ro outcrops may offer cov and shade. The rocks c form natural cisterns w collect water after rain

Animals and birds
Water sources are often indicated by animal trails and droppings or birds in flight.

Salt lakes
If a large volume of water enters a basin, a lake may develop. However, the water has a very high salt content and is undrinkable.

temperature of 6 to 8 degrees above normal (98.6°F) for any extended period can cause coma and death.

Your body attempts to dispose of this excess heat by sweating, which can lead to loss of body fluids and dehydration.

Drinking

Drink early in the morning while temperatures are low. Remember, it is the water in your body that keeps you alive, not the water in your waterbottle. Don't ration your water intake to

A member of a trans-Saharan expedition sports the correct headwear for the job: goggles to prevent sand blindness and complete protection for head and face.

little sips. That will not prevent dehydration. If you drink only enough to satisfy your thirst you can still suffer from dehydration. Your water intake must remain sufficient to make you urinate three times daily. Healthy urine is a pale straw colour.

In summer in the Sahara, you will need to drink up to 10 pints of fluid

daily. Keep your clothing on, as the insulating effect of a layer of clothes will reduce evaporation of sweat and reflect direct sunlight.

If you lie up during the heat of the day, remember that ground temperatures may be as much as 30°F hotter than the air temperature. Break through the crust of the desert into soft sand and you will find the temperature is as much as 70°F cooler at 18 inches deep. So try to rest in deep shade or between 12 and 18 inches above or below ground level. Bushmen of the Kalahari Desert urinate into holes in the ground and lie in them in the heat of the day to reduce sweating.

Don't smoke or breathe through an open mouth. This exposes the mucous membrane to the dry atmosphere, increasing your rate of dehydration. Reduce conversation for the same reason.

Finding water

If you are near a water supply, stay there and set up ground-to-air distress signals. If you have to keep moving, look for signs that indicate the direction of a water supply.

Don't rely entirely on wild animals as a guide to water in the Sahara. Some are so adapted that they do not need a regular water intake as we do. Dorcas gazelles, gerboas and gerbils, for example, extract all the moisture they need from their foodstuffs. Foxes, jackals and hyenas, however,

do not stray too far from a water supply.

Listen for the sounds of birds and baboons at early morning or evening. Quail fly towards water in the evening and away from it in the morning. Doves use the water both morning and evening, but it may be a long way off. Some turtle doves will fly 50 – 75 kilometres to water.

Man, on foot, and camels will eventually lead to water – but remember that a camel can walk vast distances between water stops.

In camels, the water is stored in the stomach and Arabs in dire straits have been known to kill the animal and use this store of water.

Don't make the mistake of thinking that tyre tracks will lead to water – you could mistakenly follow your own tracks or those of someone else equally lost. In some parts of the Sahara the "main" road is as much as 10 miles wide.

Study the rock in your surroundings; sandstone will absorb water after a rainstorm, basalt-type rocks will pool it on the surface.

Dry stream beds, known as wadis, sometimes have water below the surface. Finding it is the problem. Look for greenery on the outside of a bend in a water course, and dig at its lowest point. You may need to dig to 6ft.

If you do find water, think before you camp in the wadi itself. If it rains, wadis fill up with remarkable speed and become raging torrents.

Movement by night
In most deserts, moving by night is so hazardous as to be not a viable option.

Equipment
Radios and other sensitive items of equipment are likely to go US when exposed to direct sunlight in the desert.

Mountain deserts
High altitude deserts have thin air and little or no vegetation. Sunburn is a real danger, and movement at altitude requires extra physical exertion.

Dehydration
Keep activity to a minimum during the day to minimise water loss. Take sips of water often rather than normal drinking or gulping.

Temperature variation
The temperature may vary from as much as 130 degrees during the day down to 50 degrees at night: warm clothes are essential. Obviously, work or travel at night requires less water than day but may be more hazardous.

The burning sand
The temperature of the desert sand and rock averages 30 to 40 degrees more than that of the air, so if the air temperature is 110 then the sand would be around 140. You will be unable to walk around without adequate foot protection.

Convoy
Never attempt to cross a desert area in a single vehicle; always travel in convoy.

Collecting and Purifying the Desert's Water

Desert wells are usually not marked on the map or on the ground, and can be up to 70 metres deep. They are also prone to collapse, as the sides of the well are not shored up or supported.

The one thing deserts lack is water – so the vital thing you need to know to survive in the Sahara is how to find, purify and manage your water supplies. It is, surprisingly enough, not difficult to find water in the Sahara, although there won't be much of it. And once you have if, you need to make sure it's drinkable.

The desert still

The first attempts to extract moisture from air pockets within the desert sand were carried out simultaneously and independently at opposite ends of the world. Today, we accept the desert survival still as being a normal aid to survival in any desert.

To make a still, dig a hole roughly 3 ft square and 2 ft deep. Put a container at the bottom of the hole. Then put the end of a drinking tube at the bottom of the container. Cover the hole with a polythene sheet about 6 ft square, threading the drinking tube under the edge of the sheeting. Then seal it all round the edge of the hole with sand or stones.

Let the sheet "belly in" – you can help by placing a stone in the centre of the sheet. This creates an inverted cone over the container at the bottom of the pit. The polythene must not touch the sides of the pit, or the container itself. If it does, the condensed fluid will be wasted.

Theoretically, the sun's rays heat the ground inside the hole and cause the moisture trapped inside to evaporate. The moisture then saturates the confined air space and condenses on the cooler surface of the plastic sheet. This runs down into the container, where you can drink it through the drinking tube without having to destroy the still.

A still like this can produce up to a litre of water a day in some parts of the desert. In other areas very little is produced at all, unless you add greenery or urine in the evaporation space under the plastic sheet.

1 Select a site where you think the soil is most likely to contain moisture, such as a stream bed where the sunlight hits it most of the day. Then dig a hole three feet across by two feet deep.

2 Dig a sump in the centre of the hole with your container set into it supported by the surrounding soil.

3 Anchor the tube to the bottom of the container by forming an overhand knot loosely in the tubing. The free end of the tube is laid over the outside of the hole and the hole covered in plastic sheeting.

4 Anchor the edges of the sheet with earth and place a stone in the middle. Allow the plastic to lower into the hole until the inverted cone is 30 cm into the hole and then anchor it with more earth round the sides.

5 Make sure that the apex of the cones is directly over the container. Also make sure that the plastic cone does not touch the sides of the hole. After a few hours, you should have something to drink from the tube. Remember to plug the tube when not in use.

When it rains in the desert you must be ready to take advantage of it. In this case, it provided the rare chance of a bath in a rock pool at dawn. Remember that all arid regions have areas where the surface soil has a high mineral content, e.g. borax, salt, alkali and lime. Materiel in contact with such a surface will wear out very quickly and the water is usually undrinkable. If you wash or wet your uniform in this water it can cause crippling skin rashes.

Building a desert shelter

This shelter reduces the midday heat by as much as 30 to 40 degrees. However, it does take more time and effort to build than other shelters, so build it during the cool night to prevent increased dehydration during the day.

Construction

1 Find a low spot or depression between the dunes or dig a trench 18 to 24 inches deep, and long and wide enough for you to lie down in.

2 Pile the sand from the trench around three sides to form a mound.
3 On the open end of the trench, dig out more so that you can get in and out easily.
4 Cover the trench with material such as a parachute or poncho.
5 Secure the cover in place using sand or rocks as weights.

You can reduce the temperature of the shelter further by adding an extra layer 12 to 18 inches above the first, creating an airspace between the two layers as shown.

18 to 24 inches deep   airspace   poncho   sand anchor

poncho liner or parachute

Survival

Purifying water

Filter dirty water through several layers of cloth or a Millbank bag to remove solids. Even radioactive fall-out can be removed in this manner.

Purifying the water involves killing the germs. To do this, use purifying agents such as Puritabs, Halzone, Chloromine T., iodine, permanganate of potash, or simply boil it for between three and five minutes.

Add charcoal while the water is boiling to remove disagreeable colours. Agitate it to restore its taste, or add a small pinch of salt.

There are many chemical purifiers, and the choice is a matter of personal taste. Generally, the water needs to stand for up to 30 minutes to allow the chemical time to act properly.

Carrying water

If you have any control over your circumstances, think about how you will carry your water supply. Always take 25 per cent more than you think you need, in several containers of unbreakable material. Glass and thin plastic containers are non-starters. Conventional military water bottles in tough plastic or aluminium are reliable, as are some of the civilian versions.

Avoid carrying single one- or two-gallon containers. Desert terrains are unforgiving – a slip can result in all your water supply being lost.

A condom from your survival kit (carried inside a sock for additional support) makes an excellent portable container.

The mirage effect makes it difficult to identify an object from a distance. The effect will also blur distant range contours so that it looks like you are surrounded by a sheet of water with any elevations appearing like islands in the sea. This is not a mirage but a desert flood produced by the infrequent but sometimes very heavy rain.

At one time the US Army and the Israeli defence forces thought that they could condition their men to survive and fight on less water by gradually reducing their water intake during training. This water discipline caused hundreds of heat casualties. You simply cannot limit your water intake in this environment; you can only affect the rate at which your body loses water, so what you do not carry with you you will have to find. This expedition, part of Operation Raleigh, is carrying water testing equipment to assess all water sources on the route across the Sahara.

Water purification

Treat all water in the Sahara, no matter where from, as suspect. That includes the tap water.

Virtually any water, despite its appearance, can be made drinkable. If necessary, start by straining the supply through a Millbank bag or several layers of material to remove any suspended matter. To purify it, you must boil it for at least three minutes, or treat it with a chemical purifier and leave it to stand for 30 minutes or so.

It is possible to use your still to purify suspect water, as little solid matter or bacteria will transfer to the surface of the polythene sheet during evaporation. Bear in mind that the sheet itself may not be free of contamination.

Iraqi soldiers give water to Iranian prisoners. Tests have shown that a man performing hard work in the sun at 110°F will need at least five gallons of water a day. On the battlefield, such a demand for water will put considerable stress on the logistic back-up and therefore any sources of water in forward areas should be fully exploited.

Native wells are excellent water sources but you should purify the water as far as possible by boiling and then adding Puritabs.

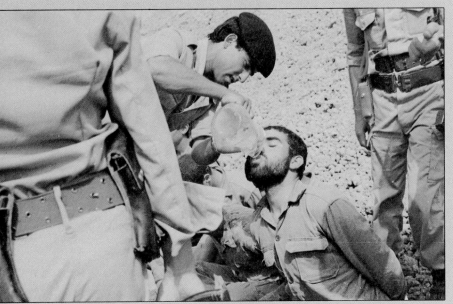

Proprietary Chemical Purifiers

Chloromine T: ⅜th inch of matchstick loaded for 5 gallon can.
Tincture of iodine: 3 drops per litre of water.
Household bleach (5.25% sodium hypochlorite): 2 drops per litre for clear water, 4 drops for cloudy water. Water will taste of chlorine.
Puritab: 1 small tablet for 1 litre bottle.
1 large tablet for 5 gallon can.
Potassium Permanganate: enough to colour the water pink.

The penalty you will pay for not purifying your water properly or neglecting to prepare food carefully, or for lack of hygiene generally, is a severely upset stomach. This in turn can lead to dehydration and heat illness through loss of body fluids. Treat an upset stomach with a proprietary preparation or, if you don't have one, use crushed charcoal or burnt, crushed bone. Neither tastes very pleasant but both are effective. The tannic acid in a very strong brew of tea will also help. Continue to drink plenty of fluids during treatment.

Desert Hazards

Operating in the desert requires a high standard of personal admin and good organisation on the part of military units. In addition to the problems posed by the climate, the local wildlife can be a serious threat to your survival.

Above: A sand viper stares inscrutably at the camera as it burrows in the sand. Very well camouflaged, the sand viper and other snakes will often enter your camp at night, so be on your guard in the morning.

Many of the creatures that live in the desert are potentially dangerous, from bats and snakes to scorpions and centipedes — and even dogs and spiders. Heat exhaustion, malaria, and storms all offer their own hazards as well.

Once bitten

On your own in the desert, avoid suspect animals at all times.

Rabies virus is carried in the saliva of an infected animal and enters your body through breaks in the skin. Even a lick from a friendly but infected animal can infect you through a cut or abrasion. Potential carriers include dogs, foxes, cats, bats and some types of rodent.

If you are bitten by *any* animal, get a tetanus booster as soon as possible.

Scorpion stings

There are two common types of potentially lethal scorpion in the Sahara: *Androctonus australis* and *Buthus occiutanus* (also known as Fat Tailed scorpion because of its massive tail), which is often cited as the world's most dangerous. Drop for drop, their venom is as toxic as that of a cobra and can kill a man in four hours. If the scorpion stings in self-defence it will usually inject the maximum dose of poison.

Symptoms

The sting of a buthid scorpion produces intense pain at the site of the sting, often without discoloration apart from a small area of gooseflesh. A feeling of tightness then develops in the throat, so that the victim tries to clear imaginary phlegm. The tongue feels thick, and speech becomes difficult. The casualty becomes restless, with involuntary twitching of the muscles.

Sneezing bouts and a runny nose follow. There is an uncontrolled flow of saliva, which may become frothy. The heart rate will increase, followed by convulsions. The extremities turn blue before the casualty dies. The whole sequence of events may take as little as 45 minutes or as long as 12 hours.

Snakes

Snakes are permanent residents in most parts of the desert. They hibernate, however, and so you'll see fewer

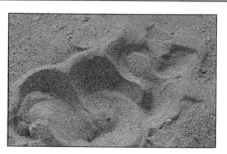

Snake sign: this swirling pattern is produced by a sand viper burrowing into the desert. He can also flatten himself out and glide across the sand with bewildering speed.

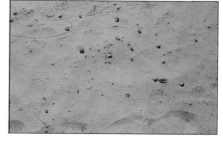

A snake moving along the surface of the sand will leave a characteristic trail as it pushes part of its body against the ground.

snakes in winter.

Most are venomous, so regard any snake bite as suspect and treat it as promptly as possible. Simple precautions against snake bite include shaking out boots and sleeping bags before you use them, and using a torch after dark.

Don't go barefoot: certain types of snake actually bury themselves in the sand, leaving only their nostrils and eyes showing. They ambush their prey – including you – in this fashion and are extremely difficult to spot.

If you get bitten by a snake, study the pattern of teeth punctures. If there are two well-defined punctures, the bite will be that of one of the viper group. Non-poisonous snakes with solid fangs, and mildly venomous back-fanged snakes, made a horseshoe-shaped row of teeth marks.

It takes only 5 mg of venom from the Saw Scale viper to kill a man. As with scorpion stings, defensive bites tend to contain the maximum amount of venom.

However, not every snake bite is fatal. You're more likely to survive a bite to the shin than one deep in the muscular tissues of the thigh or calf.

Treatment for snake bite.

Ideally, a snake bite casualty should be immobilised and given sedatives. Ice is put on the bite site, and a tourniquet applied and loosened at frequent intervals, and the casualty evacuated to hospital for treatment with antivenene, adrenalin and plasma. The snake is killed for hospital identification.

In reality, you will probably be able only to attempt to restrict the amount and rate of venom entering the blood stream, by applying a tourniquet between the bite and heart. The tourniquet must not cut off the blood supply entirely – this can cause tissue damage, and possibly gangrene and kidney failure. Release the pressure each half-hour until you get help.

The patient must also be rested as much as possible, and kept calm. Panic can become a major problem – it increases the heart rate and so speeds the circulation of the venom in the blood. Physical exertion must also be avoided.

Opinions differ on whether to "cut and suck" or not. This treatment may worsen the situation, as any wound inside the mouth will allow the venom to enter into the system.

When you're on your own, there may be some value in cutting and bleeding as an alternative to simply sitting and hoping that the snake was

Bizarre rock formations in Algeria have been created by the fierce desert wind blowing sand against the rock and sculpting it into a good set for a science fiction movie.

The desert is also the land of instant vegetation. Pop-up fungus materialises almost overnight after a rainstorm in southern Algeria. This is a shaggy inkcap, which is edible raw.

The hard, rocky surface of the desert makes artillery and mortar fire extemely effective with each explosion producing a shower of rocky fragments in addition to the shrapnel.

not venomous. You can easily shed a pint of blood without any ill effects, and this may be all you need to do to save your life.

Simply cut yourself deep enough to bleed freely with a clean knife at both entry points. Then wash the cut in a solution of potassium permanganate. Do not urinate into the cut.

Overheating and water loss

The maximum water loss your body can tolerate is probably as high as 20 per cent. However, 12 per cent is a more practical maximum. You won't be capable of making rational decisions after losing a fifth of your body fluids.

Upset stomachs can be a major cause of dehydration. On your own in the wild, you can quickly find yourself very ill indeed. Crushed and ground charcoal, chalk or bone will provide a cure. Similarly, the tannic acid in a very strong brew of tea will help.

Two conditions can arise from overheating: heat exhaustion, and heat stroke.

Heat exhaustion usually affects people getting strenuous physical exercise in hot, humid climates. It's

Below: Camel trekking local wrapped up against the chill of the desert night preparing a brew. In many parts of the desert, firewood is a rare commodity.

caused by loss of salt and water from the body. It will be aggravated by stomach upset, diarrhoea or vomiting.

Remove the casualty to a cooler environment, and replace lost fluids and minerals. Seek medical aid.

Heat stroke is caused by a very high environmental temperature or a feverish illness (such as malaria), and leads to a greatly increased body temperature. It develops when the body can no longer control its temperature by sweating, and can occur quite suddenly.

Reduce the casualty's temperature

Survival

"I give up; where the hell are we?" 101st Airborne ('Screaming Eagles') wrestles with a navigational problem on exercise in Egypt. The lack of landmarks can make desert travel more like navigation at sea.

The camel is a temperamental beast with a deep sense of its own superiority. Muslims have suggested that this is because the camel is the only creature to know the 100th name of God. If you are going to rely on camels, it is essential to learn how to handle them first.

How to use the Mk 3 signal mirror

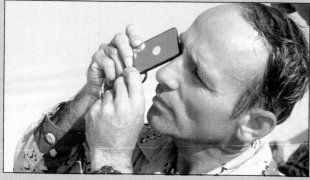

The Mk 3 signal mirror issued to US Forces is a handy heliograph which you can hang around your neck. Make sure the reflective side is against your chest when not in use.

1 Reflect sunlight from the mirror on to a nearby surface like a rock or your hand.
2 Slowly bring the mirror up to eye-level and look through the sighting hole. You will see a bright spot of light, which is the aim indicator.
3 Hold the mirror near to your eye and move it so that the aim indicator is on the target.

CAUTION: Don't flash the mirror rapidly. In a combat zone, a pilot might mistake the distant twinkling for groundfire and treat you to a rocket attack! Don't hold the light on someone's cockpit either, or you could dazzle the pilot.

Mirror signals can be seen for many miles, even in hazy weather, so keep sweeping the horizon even if nothing is in sight. In a combat zone where you could attract enemy attention you must obviously wait and positively identify an aircraft before signalling.

Above: Iraqi Special Forces training includes a survival course which emphasises the use of natural resources including the odd snake. This sort of character building exercise is a good way of sorting the wheat from the chaff.

as quickly as possible, and get medical help.

Malaria

This very debilitating illness is caused by the bite of the female *Anopheles* mosquito. The insect breeds in stagnant water. Take a course of anti-malaria tablets before you enter into an area where the disease is endemic, and continue the treatment throughout your stay in the country.

See your doctor for advice on the type of anti-malarial treatment recommended for the area. In an emergency, quinine is an effective if unpleasant treatment.

Dust storms

Generally, these are either limited to a height of about 6ft, or rise to hundreds of feet in the air. In either case, if visibility is restricted, seal all equipment likely to be affected and be prepared to sit it out. This is preferable to getting lost, or even injured, in the poor visibility.

During severe dust storms, the air temperature can soar up to 58°C (135°F), while simultaneously the

Dangerous wildlife

Egyptian cobra

Typically about 2 metres long, the Egyptian Cobra can be black, brown or yellow. Some like the one shown here are light brown with darker crossbands. They like cultivated land, rocky hillsides, old ruins and even rural villages. Their venom is a very powerful neurotoxin, i.e. it attacks your nervous system, making it hard to breathe.

Sand viper

Well camouflaged and only about 60 cm long, the Sand Viper is found throughout North Africa. Its venom is haemotoxic: it attacks your circulatory system, causing tissue damage and internal bleeding.

Camel spider

The camel spider or 'wind scorpion', as it is known to the Arabs, grows to 15-20 cm in length and has some very anti-social eating habits. When not eating its fellows, the camel spider will eat beetles, scorpions and even small lizards at great speed by injecting a venom that dissolves the internal organs of the prey and then sucking out the resultant juice.

moisture content will drop to only a few per cent. A long-lasting dust storm can cause serious dehydration: you can lose up to a quart of moisture in sweat in one hour in these conditions.

A side-effect of a prolonged severe dust storm is the rise in atmospheric electricity due to sand friction. This can cause severe headaches and nausea but can be neutralised by "earthing" yourself to the ground.

Magnetic compasses will be affected in these conditions. The wisest course will be to stay where you are. Always carry a spare compass.

These sandstone pillar formations would make movement on foot at night impossible. You must recce in the early morning any route you are planning to march, and avoid anything like this. Military engineer survey maps show the areas that are obstacles to tanks, wheeled vehicles and soldiers on foot. Without adequate information, this type of area could be the death of you.

Fighting Fit

JOINING THE RESERVE

Above: This is the much-coveted Royal Marines Reserve Commando shoulder flash, which together with the Green Beret marks you out as a Marine. Winning the right to wear this badge involves some very hard work on top of your civilian job and some real blood, sweat and tears.

A Marine recruit covers his arc on the reorganisation phase of an attack. The Royal Marine is Reserve are armed with the rather elderly and over-powered SLR, but it is a solid weapon which is still well regarded.

Since 1948, the Royal Marines Forces Volunteer Reserve and its present-day successor, the Royal Marines Reserve (RMR) has served alongside Regular Marine Commandos in all corners of the globe. There were, in 1988, some 1,240 Reservists, of whom 55 or so are ex-Regulars. Most of those in the RMR, as in the TA, are individuals without previous military experience who choose to lead civilian lives between times with their unit. A reservist can expect to serve up to one night a week and several weekends a year, in addition to an annual two-week exercise, with the RMR.

RMR training, however, is both long and arduous. It begins with the Induction Weekend, during which the applicant and the RMR will have the

opportunity to size up one another. Those who successfully complete the induction process can then be attested, whereupon training begins in earnest.

Recruit training is divided into two phases and is common to all entrants, regardless of their aspirations. Phase One, Individual Training, lasts an

The platoon moves on foot to the Bombard vedette, a very solidly constructed bunker from where they can observe what an exploding shell looks like in various sizes and fuse settings.

average of four months and is split into two stages: In-Unit, and the Phase One Course. The aim is to establish the basic foundation of knowledge and military skills on which all your later training will be based.

In-Unit/Phase One training takes place over a number of training nights during which you will learn to prepare for the RMR. It culminates with the two-week Phase One Course, held at the Commando Training Centre Royal Marines (CTCRM) in Devon. Successful recruits are rewarded with the presentation of Their royal Marines Reserve shoulder flashes.

Phase Two training builds on individual skills and teaches you to operate as part of a team. Lasting some six months, it too is divided into two stages: In-Unit Training and the Phase Two Course. The latter is another two-week course held at CTCRM, where you now have to prove yourself worthy of wearing the green beret by completing a number of tests.

You must negotiate the assault course in five minutes or less; run 200 yards in under 90 seconds in full kit while carrying a 'wounded' comrade and both weapons; complete the combined Tarzan/assault courses in under 13 minutes and march six miles as a squad within 60 minutes. You also have to accurately fire at least six out of 10 rounds on a 25-metre range after running the endurance course – all in under 71 minutes! The fortnight ends with a three-night exercise that puts into practice the skills you've acquired during the past year or so.

The best to come

Once you've successfully completed training, there is plenty to look forward to. You can expect to carry out amphibious landings and heli-assaults. You could receive specialist training as a swimmer, canoeist, driver, cook, signaller, PTI, weapons instructor, drill instructor or assault engineer. You might qualify as a parachutist, train to be a mountain and arctic warfare specialist, or perhaps become the coxswain of a landing craft or rigid raiding craft!

Whatever your choice, as a trained soldier you can expect to take part in a variety of exciting exercises both at home and abroad.

What can you expect during a weekend exercise with the RMR? Well, you might find yourself on Salisbury Plain in a field-firing exercise, involving 81-mm mortars and 105-mm light guns.

After finishing work on Friday afternoon, you turn up at your RMR Centre from where you will be transported to the training area. The last group reaches Salisbury Plain at midnight, and joins everyone else 'bivvying up'

There is no expense spared where it matters and the anti-tank platoon is fully equipped with *MILAN*, including Mira sights. This *MILAN* position has been set up for firing on a range; in war it would be dug in.

As Marines look on, a barrage of 81-mm mortar and 105-mm artillery rounds hammer the target area. Marines are equipped with their own mortar platoons and they also have commando gunner reservists with 105-mm light gun.

The firepower of the general-purpose machine-gun makes up for the lack of *SA80* and the Figure 11 targets in the area of the *MILAN* targets are shredded in a hail of 7.62-mm in an impressive firepower demonstration, watched by the Commandant General Royal Marines.

Inside the Bombard OP, Marines observe shells bursting only a few metres away. Most of the shell fragments burst forwards as the shells are coming in overhead. You can still feel the concussion from the detonating rounds through the thick vision blocks.

in a wood. The exercise proper begins on Saturday morning. While the guns register their targets, you practise fire and manoeuvre, based on the new SA80 tactics. It will be some time before the RMR is issued with the latest rifle, so you carry out the drills with SLRs. Despite this, you conduct yourself professionally, re-taking the objective again and again in an effort to perfect the new assault techniques.

Fire in the afternoon

Saturday afternoon is spent at the live-firing range. At 1300 you are treated to a spectacle rarely seen even

Fighting Fit

by the Regulars, when a MILAN team disposes of a stationary target with two rounds fired in succession. This is followed by an opportunity to see the effects of mortar and artillery fire. Sounding like jet aircraft, the 105s course overhead to detonate with a puff of grey smoke far in the distance. Seconds later, you hear the crump of the explosions.

You also contribute to the 45-minute firepower demonstration, forming up to fire SLRs and GPMGs into targets dotted about the vast area. When that's over, everyone moves into a Bombard OP from where you can view another mortar and artillery barrage, this time with the rounds landing just a few metres to your front!

The demo is followed by a lesson in artillery spotting, with an opportunity to look through a MILAN simulator, a laser rangefinder and the optics of an SA80 sight. What a day!

There is plenty to chat about on the route back to the bivvy area and afterwards, as you prepare 'scran' from your 24-hour ration packs. Then it's heads down until 0800 the next day.

Assault on Sunday

At 0845, everyone leaves the wood for the short yomp to the live-firing area, where you are to take part in a two-stage company attack. The move up to the start line takes you through a grassy meadow, with each section advancing in extended line. It is a memorable scene.

You arrive at a small wood, where the officers gather to discuss the coming operation. Everyone is confident and looking forward to events – although the Major in command of the guns seems a little nervous that his rounds might somehow fall short!

In the event, the exercise goes off without a hitch. You advance towards two objectives, with artillery and mor-

Above: The mortar platoon from Merseyside fire 81-mm mortar at night. You may be part-time, but you cannot afford to be any less efficient than the regulars when it comes down to lobbing HE bombs around the training area.

tar fire suppressing the 'enemy' prior to your assault. When you withdraw, the 81-mm and 105-mm rounds obliterate any 'enemy' foolhardy enough to counter-attack. A great way to end the morning.

And, next weekend, those able to make it have an amphibious exercise in Scotland to look forward to!

Above: Marines from the rifle companies are instructed on the MILAN simulator so that they will have a fair idea of how to operate the weapon in addition to the members of the anti-tank platoon.

Left: A Marine gun team wait for the order to move off from the section commander on a live firing attack. Helmets are not camouflaged as part of the safety restrictions.

There are five RMR centres dotted throughout the United Kingdom. With the exception of RMR *Tyne*, each acts as HQ for a number of Detachments. RMR *London* has two: Chatham and Portsmouth. RMR *Bristol* commands the Poole, Lympstone, Cardiff and Plymouth Detachments. Manchester Detachment comes under the command of RMR *Merseyside*, and RMR Scotland, with its HQ in *Glasgow*, is responsible for Dundee, Grangemouth and Greenock.

Combat Report
Oman:
Driving to Defa

A former member of a Royal Corps of Transport team attached to 22 SAS Regiment describes an incident in Oman in the mid-1970s.

The SAS had been very active in the last couple of weeks, but apart from routine troop moves and the daily passage of fresh rations to the various positions we were having a quiet life. One evening at Prayers (briefing) I was asked to drive an unscheduled ration truck to the Defa position, about 120 miles away.

Half the journey would be on a fairly good tarmac road laid by the British Royal Engineers and the rest across dirt track and desert. It promised to be interesting. The SAS had an RCT section attached to them on general driving duties, and one of these, Tony, volunteered to ride shotgun as my co-driver.

We drew extra ammo and grenades from the supply dump and gave our wagon a good service: the last thing I wanted was to break down in the desert. We were driving an armoured half cab – the cab of a standard four-ton truck with something resembling a mess tin on top, open for easy access and fitted with a roll bar. Armoured plates instead of mudguards to protect against shrapnel splash and a layer of sandbags on the floor completed the job.

RCT regulations state that you should never mix potentially dangerous loads, but this was wartime so all that was thrown out of the window. Our load consisted of four drums of high octane aviation fuel and several containers of 81-mm mortar rounds. We also carried a few luxuries, including soft toilet rolls, presumably for the officers. The six other trucks in the convoy consisted of four-ton water bowsers, also converted to half cabs and driven by Jash (Arab army) drivers.

We set off in the early hours, before the sun had risen properly, to give us a cool start. The greenery of Salalah gave way to the harsh sandy brown of the foothills. And so the drive continued. As far as the eye could see there was a moon landscape, with small pebbles and broken ground that would suddenly give way to deep wadis, the road detouring for many miles before finding a way down and up the other side. Then came miles of cracked ground as if a giant lake had suddenly dried up; this was followed by miles of white salt lake. Then the whole thing would repeat itself.

The first leg of the journey was not too bad, being on a semi-decent road, but before long we turned left off the road on to a rough dirt track.

Several miles later, having stopped to dig out two of the water trucks that had strayed from the firm ground, we reached a low but prominent hill. Sitting on top was the welcome sight of a Saladin armoured car. It was crewed by Arabs but had a white officer. He came over to meet us as the convoy ground to a halt. Taking advantage of the impromptu stop, most of the Arab drivers took cover from the sun under the shade of their trucks and promptly fell asleep. The Saladin commander told us to follow him to the forward artillery position, known simply as Gunlines.

We took a welcome drink from our goatskin water choggles while we waited for the Arabs to remount, and then set off. Because of the dust we were forced to follow at a distance. Even though we adopted the Arab style of head-dress and wore sand goggles we still had to stop from time to time to rub the sand out of our eyes.

We soon reached the artillery. They consisted of 5.5 medium field howitzers and some ageing 35-pdr guns. A spattering of British officers and NCOs controlled the Arab gunners and were quite proud of the fact that their guns were taking on Soviet guns and Sagger and Katyushka missiles and effectively beating them. Our Saladin handed us over to another vehicle to take us the last mile to Defa.

One huge salvo of gunfire

We were told by the new officer that it would be a few minutes before we could set off as Defa was just receiving its daily stonking from the enemy; they were at that time receiving nearly 150 incoming shells a day. We could just make out the smoke on the skyline.

Suddenly a great roar to one side of us caused us all to duck as Gunlines erupted into one huge salvo of gunfire in support of Defa. For a few seconds we were blinded and deafened by the noise and smoke around us. Then as quickly as it had started the firing stopped.

"Prepare to move"

"Prepare to move."

Off we went. It was much harder going this time as the hard rock now gave way to deep, soft sand. The Saladin came alongside as we negotiated a particularly tough bit of ground.

"Stay as close as you can to my tyre tracks," he said. This was easier said than done as the tracks disappeared as soon as they were made.

As we got closer to the position we could see the outlines of the sangars and gun pits. Smoke drifted lazily into the air where some of the incoming shells had hit their mark. As we arrived into the main position we were met by a bearded SAS trooper, who was more interested in whether we had brought them any strawberry jam than how many mortar bombs we had on board. He had just built a new desert oven out of ammo boxes and was very keen to make some jam tarts.

"The last one got a direct hit; I wouldn't have minded, but there was a loaf in it," he said.

As the tankers offloaded their water into the storage tanks we reversed up to the mortar pits to replenish their ammo. I had to manoeuvre around a crater with a peculiar-looking pipe sticking out of it.

Unmarked minefields

"Mind that, son, it's one of this morning's Katyushkas. We haven't had time to disarm it yet."

One trooper had a brew on the go and we were invited to have a cup of tea. Sitting down on the sandbagged wall of the gun pit, we had a chance to look around. Craters were everywhere and smoke was coming from the remains of a gun pit which, luckily, had contained nobody at the time of the direct hit. We could see the enemy-held area in the distance. Nothing spectacular; one range of hills looked like another.

We were asked if we had lost any trucks; I said no. Even I couldn't get lost on two straight roads with no junctions.

"No, you idiot – did you lose any on the mines?"

We looked at each other. So that was why we had been told to keep in the Saladin's tracks. Dust or no dust, I was going to be up his exhaust pipe on the way back. It seemed that the Iranians, who were at this time on our side, had planted about 130 anti-tank mines forward of their position. When the SAS and their support teams arrived they found that the Iranians had not marked the minefield accurately on their maps. Every now and again one of our vehicles would find a mine.

It had happened recently to two troopers travelling in a half cab. The truck lost its radiator and front axle, and apart from concussion the troopers got away with it.

All too soon we had to leave. As the convoy pulled out behind our armoured support we left them busily putting down a wall of covering fire for us of 81-mm white phosphorus: the rounds that we had just delivered. Turning to Tony, I said, "Now that's what I call job satisfaction."

The "peculiar-looking pipe" is a Soviet 122-mm 'Katyushka' rocket which landed next to the mortar pit but did not explode. Another one scored a direct hit on a British gun pit but fortunately no-one was in it at the time.

An SAS mortar team in action. We were supplying them with 81-mm mortar rounds and we were also carrying some drums of high octane aviation spirit which was an exciting combination of loads to have in the back of the truck.

Fighting Fit

AMPHIBIOUS WARFARE

*Geminis speed through the sheltered waters of the loch carrying a search and destroy team ashore. Unlike other **TA** units Royal Marine reservists have their skills tested to the full on annual deployment exercises in **Norway**.*

A Gemini is unloaded for action from the support boat. The Gemini is fast and very manoeuvrable with a top speed of 12 knots fully loaded or 18 knots when empty.

The Royal Marines Reserve is intended to provide Regular units with additional personnel, including battle casualty replacements, in time of war, and is also committed to protect key installations in the UK. What makes the RMR that extra bit special, when compared with the TA, is its annual deployment to Norway. Here, by 1990, RMR should be able to provide fully trained arctic warfare troops as part of 3 Commando Brigade. This latter force consists of the 200-strong T Company Group (RMR).

Besides T Company Group, other formed RMR sub-units include 2 Raiding Troop RMR; 4 Troop SBS (R); various Home Defence sub-units and 608 TACP (R) (four men only). After qualifying as a Royal Marine Reservist you can serve in one of these units as a Specialist. What can you expect if, for example, you opt for 2 Raiding Troop?

See the world

As coxswain of a Gemini raiding craft you will be responsible for the maintenance and operation of the rubber boat and its 35 hp Johnson outboard motor. Your skills will be put to the test during regular training exercises, working with general duty Marines anywhere from the south of England and the west coast of Scotland to the fjords of Norway and the coastal waters of Belize.

A typical weekend begins with everyone reporting to the RMR Detachment at Greenock, where the lochs of Strathclyde provide a picturesque setting for a proposed two-day amphibious exercise. The operation is designed to test tactical movement and command and control – from troop HQ, down to section level.

After many hours of travelling (some of you don't arrive until 0400 on Saturday), you are allowed surprisingly little time to prepare your craft – but then, that's what you'd expect in a real war! RTM is set for 0630. However, you are still putting together your Geminis at 0620. Orders, originally planned for 0730, are now put back to 0800. By then everyone is finally ready.

The brief is that a road north of nearby Loch Long has been occupied by enemy forces, (provided by 23 SAS). Small units, consisting of between 10 and 15 four-man observation posts, are now pushing south. The enemy is equipped with up to two dozen amphibious vehicles, indicating that they probably intend to launch a third attack axis from the loch. South of the steadily advancing enemy is an RMR company on a search-and-destroy mission which, having sustained casualties, needs to be ferried out in order to reorganise.

First task

The raiding troop OC, therefore, will RV with the search-and-destroy group to arrange a troop lift to their intended destination. Having done that, the troop will set up its own forward operating base (FOB) and stand-by for further orders.

For the exercise, the Geminis will operate during daylight. Were you in actual combat you would, of course, expect to work entirely at night.

At 0830 you learn that three boats from RMR Merseyside will not be able to make it. The attitude of a few seems to be, "Well, that's it. We can't carry on without them!" But you have to expect foul-ups and, as in any Regular unit, you have to work around them. The exercise will carry on, regardless of the missing craft. You start moving out at 0940.

You take a pass boat that will carry the troop from Greenock into Loch Long. Your Geminis are either towed behind the tug-like vessel or piled on the deck, below the wheelhouse. It takes an hour to reach your destination.

The OC then takes two Geminis to find the search-and-destroy team. They are quickly located, waiting patiently on a nearby midge-infested shore. A short while later, more Geminis arrive to ferry the weary troops to another location, the landings closely watched by the CO RMR Scotland moored closeby in his private yacht.

Meanwhile, the company commander is forced to cut short his participation in the exercise and command of the fighting company is handed over to the CSM. While he organises his men for clearance patrols, you take your boats to another beach chosen as the FOB. After hauling the Geminis ashore, you quickly set up your shelters before crawling inside for some welcome shut-eye.

Sunset patrol

At 1830 hrs yours is one of a pair of boats detailed to pick up a patrol. It is a lovely, warm evening – ideal for a high-speed trip through the sheltered waters of the loch. The 20-minute

Below: These Marines are looking pleased to get away from shore and the insect life. Note the size of the Berghaus Bergens: one feature of infantry life is carrying serious weight over rugged countryside for long periods.

The officer commanding the Second Raiding Troop and the administrative and training officers go ashore from the pass boat to RV with the search and destroy company.

Above: Marines break cover to board the Gemini which transports them away from the midge-infested shoreline. The GPMG team cover the rest of the section while they leap aboard.

Fighting Fit

the rest of the way.

Amphibious operations are particularly complicated at night, and identifying the drop-off point isn't easy. Once everything is under control, a short yomp takes the 'gravs' along a forest road, towards the enemy position. When contact is made, the subsequent firefight is vicious and prolonged, until the Marines are ordered to withdraw back along the same road.

Then there's further confusion, when the rear element runs into an ambush! The sergeant major, leading the withdrawal, is in a quandary. In real life, if assistance were required it would, of course, be given without question. However, the RV with the boats has to be made by somebody, so the sergeant major decides to push on towards the beach-head. The rear element arrives shortly after.

Pick-up is at 0400. An hour later, the pass boat arrives back at Greenock where you hose the boats down and sort equipment prior to your departure. It is Monday tomorrow, and for most of you, the start of another 'working' week!

Above: The raiding party arrive in their new location and pile out trying to avoid wet feet. This may seem a trivial point but boots, wet feet and heavy Bergens do not mix and the exercises may not give you time to sort out a sock change. Water softened feet are easily blistered and damaged.

Left: A machine gunner keeps watch while his mates settle in a few yards off the beach.

journey is an exhilarating experience, and makes you glad to be a member of raiding troop.

As your Gemini skims across the calm surface, you have ample time to admire the impressive scenery of forest-covered hills, their subtle hues brought to life by the light of the setting sun. You wonder if the patrol you're picking up, eaten alive by midges while sweltering beneath the weight of weapons and kit, feels the same sense of well-being! Probably not, you decide, catching sight of the unsmiling group awaiting your arrival.

Grim expressions soon change to smiles, however, as you steer your group away from shore and out into the loch, where the refreshing spray and welcome breeze quickly blows away even the most determined midges. Oh well, guys, you should have joined the raiding troop!

Night attack

Little else is scheduled until midnight, when the Geminis are to ferry the Marines to another location for a raid against the enemy, who are resting in their harbour area. After steering to a point off the beach-head, all motors are cut. In silence, you paddle

Above: This is the orders group for the officers and senior NCOs involved in the night raid against an enemy position.

Right: When the exercise is over you cannot relax until you have prepared your kit ready to go again. Post exercise administration is just what you need after a hard exercise to completely finish you off for work on Monday morning!

Above: These Marines are all smiles on the route back. No problem here in near perfect conditions. Operationally you could be going out in very rough weather, at night and carrying enough kit in your fighting order to sink you and the life jacket.